Influence

Workbook

Intro

Kate Pickering

Macmillan Education Limited
4 Crinan Street
London N1 9XW

Companies and representatives throughout the world

Influence Workbook Intro ISBN 978-1-380-03273-7
Influence Workbook Intro with Student's App ISBN 978-1-380-06777-7

Written by Kate Pickering

The author has asserted their right to be identified as the author of this work in accordance with the Copyright, Designs and Patents Act 1988.

First published 2021

Original design by Designers Collective Ltd and emc design ltd
Page make-up by emc design ltd
Illustrated by Dani Geremia (Beehive Illustration) pp151, 153, 156; Janos Jantner (Beehive Illustration) pp137, 141, 143, 145; Tamara Joubert (Beehive Illustration) pp7, 27; Carl Morris (Beehive Illustration) pp24, 67, 139; Laszlo Veres (Beehive Illustration) p50; Nuno Alexandre Viera (Beehive Illustration) pp11, 42, 59
Cover design by Designers Educational
Cover photographs by Getty Images/Artic-Images, Getty Images/ monkeybusinessimages
Picture research by Julie-anne Wilce
Cover research by Penelope Bowden, Proudfoot Pictures

The author and publishers would like to thank the following for permission to reproduce their photographs:
From the Alamy Stock Photo collection: Album p121(tl), ATHENA PICTURE AGENCY LTD p75(br), BFA pp18(cl), 121(tc)(tr), Richard G. Bingham II p47(tl), Collection Christophel p18(c), chrisstockphoto p73(tr), CTK p35(br), dpa picture alliance p23(b), dbphots p112(t), Everett Collection Inc pp21(tr), 67(tr), Paul Christian Gordon p148(br), Hero Images Inc p133(tr), Image Professionals GmbH p100(bcl), Jon Arnold Images Ltd p100(tl)(tc), Jeffrey Mayer p58(5), MBI p57(tr), myLAM p12(bl), peterforsberg p12(bcl), PictureLux/The Hollywood Archive p18(tc), Boaz Rottem p33(tr), Science History Images p148(bc), Tetra Images p68(5), Rob Walls p108(tr); **Andy Kelvin** p149(cr); **Bye Bye Plastic Bags** p65(tr)(cr); **Getty Images** p5(6), ALAMA p5(4.1), aimy27feb p44(8), Akabei p103(b), amnachphoto p44(3), Antagain p107(a), anzeletti p144(5), arturbo p5(3.2), Ascent Xmedia p21(t), Babylon and Beyond Photography/Vicki Jauron p43(br), Richard Bailey p36(2), barisonal p107(2), Caspar Benson p129(cr), Alistair Berg p133(b), BetNoire p107(f), Blend Images/Jamie Grill p127(3), bonetta p69(jacket), bhofack2 p74(5), Busà Photography p105(a), Charlie4mav p148(tr), chengyuzheng p102(4), choness p107(e), Chromacome p26(2), Martial Colomb p131(br), Tanya Constantine p11(tr), Robert Daly p36(6), da-kuk p123(t), Roberto David p39(b), David Merron Photography p37(tcl), Peter Dazeley p132(c), Bruno De Hogues p113(t), deepblue4you p76(tl), DGLimages p79(cl), Danita Delimont p148(br), Kevin Dodge pp4(br), 136(bl), Rodin Eckenroth p58(1), Effi p117(tl), Eivaisla p10(8), ewg3D p105(c), EyeEm p102(3), EyeEm/ Joaquin Corbalan p52(4.1), EyeEm/Adha Ghazali p74(9), Fotosearch p127(4), Brian A Jackson p107(1), EyeEm/Christine Korten p44(4), EyeEm/Sommai Larkjit p102(2), EyeEm/Ng Sok Lian p107(c), EyeEm/Henk Ten Napel p68(2), EyeEm/Michele Palmia p150(c), EyeEm/Natdanai Pankong p10(6), EyeEm/ Craig Russell p102(1), EyeEm/Xrrth Choti Thaen Sila p107(d), Flashpop p147(bl), Francesco Carta fotografo p135(br), fstop123 p20(cr), Tetiana Garkusha p102(8), Georgina198 p5(6.2), Stuart Gleave p5(5.2), Global Stock p117(tr), GoodLifeStudio p68(6), Anna Gorin p17(bl), gorodenkoff p46(cl), Heather Harrahan p144(cr), Hill Street Studios p135(cl), Andrew Hounslow p26(7), Belinda Howell p68(1), igoriss p44(bl), Image Source p50(cr), Imagesbybarbara p127(5), Imgorthand p133(cr), isitsharp p132(a), Jacobs Stock Photography Ltd pp119(tr), 125, Joylmage p38, jpbcpa p36(4), kali9 pp36(3), 45(cr), 154(br), karandaev p102(7), kate_sept2004 pp23(cr), 53(tr), Sharie Kennedy p36(1), Ishii Koji p53(tl), Gerard Koudenburg p35(cow), Lucy Lambriex p23(a), Lingxiao Xie p30(b), Warren Little p54(tr), ljubaphoto p133(cr), lolostock p47(cr), MarioGuti p74(2), MarsBars p119(tl), Letizia McCall p74(6), Daniel McGarrah p106(1), Simon McGill p10(7), Media News Group/Pasadena Star-News via p61(br), Media Production p68(3), Wako Megumi p102(6), Eduardo Mendez p12(tr), mikroman6 p105(e), Mirrorpix p59(c), mixetto pp35(5), 152(mother), Moelyn Photos p35(tcr), monkeybusinessimages pp39(a), 124(cl), Moonstone Images p35(bcl), morpheuse p30(a), Morsa Images pp19(br), 127(2), Aldo Murillo p110(tr), Sean Murphy p135(tr), Aleksandar Nakic p132(b), Nanette J.Stevenson-ebbystouch.com p115(t), Natikka p107(b), Neustockimages p69(tr), Nick Brundle Photography p103(a), NurPhoto p55(tl), Andrew Olney p27(cl), omersukrugoksu p5(3.1), onurdongel p48(tr), Pavliha p122(c), Douglas Pearson p100(tr), Anna Pekunova p124(c), photomanx21 p144(4), popovaphoto p52(6.2), Simon Potter p18(cr), Mike Powell p71(cl), QOcreative p70(tl), Zen Rial p107(4), Ridofranz p147(bc), Rixipix p37(tl), Anthony Rosenberg p102(5), Andy Sacks p106(2), Sarenac p26(5), Guillaume Sequin p5(1.2), Paul Simcock p147(br), Sissoupitch p105(b), Somrakjendee p52(1.1), Stringer/Jemal Countess p58(3), Syntheticmessiah p103(c), Karl Tapales pp26(8), 52(2.1), TraceRouda p15(cl), Kentaroo Tryman p106(5), george tsartsianidis p102(9), urfinguss p144(c), Klaus Vedfelt p111(t), View Stock p70(c), wat p103(d), Wavebreakmedia p152(boy), Weekend Images Inc. p109(t), Westend61 pp14(t), 26(6), 69(br), 127(1), wulingyun p129(c), xavierarnau p74(4), Yagi Studio p116(c), Brian Yarvin p26(4), zimindmitry p69(trousers), zoranm p102(10); **Macmillan Education Ltd** pp60, 66(br), Sergio Azenha p52(7.2), Blend Images p73(7), Judith Collins p52(5.2), Tony Cordoza p52(1.2), Everett Collection Inc p25(tr), Chris Fredriksson p69(bus), Jimmie48 Photography p41(tr), Magone p129(cl), Getty Images p26(1), blackred p74(8), fortise p52(3.2), Don Hammond p29(cl), Hemera/Thinkstock Images p69(train), iStockphoto pp35(dolphin), 44(5)(6), 52(4.2), 69(T-shirt), 77(a)(c)(d), 129(nuts)(tl)(br)(tr), iStockphoto/Thinkstock Images p44(2), mbbirdy/Matjaz Boncina p106(4), MCCAIG p77(b), Mosutatsu p5(5.1), narvikk p5(7), Nora Carol Photography p125(tr), Paul Panayiotou p78(tr), popovaphoto p52(2.2), Rundstedt B. Rovillos p35(tr), serts p5(1.1), Ariel Skelley p106(3), svetikd p15(c), Marin Tomas p69(car), Thinkstock Images p5(2.1), Westend61 pp35(elephant), 37(tl), vladimir zakharov p13(br), Image Source pp74(1), 107(3), iStockphoto p129(bc), Shutterstock p74(10), Kucher Serhii p125(tl), studiocasper p44(1), Westend61 p50; **Marley Dias** p62(tl); **Gillian Milner** p54(cr); **Shutterstock.com**/ADragan p45(c), akiyoko p10(5), Aviavlad p26(9), Yingna Cai p100(tcl), CREATISTA p15(tr), Steve Cukrov p15(bl), Joanne Davidson p19(bl), Oleg Doroshin p52(6.1), fromBake pp5(2.2), 26(3), Funlovingukrainian p52(3.1), gfdunt p129(books), Javvani p117(c), Aneta Karnecka p100(br), Kletr p10(1), Kondor83 p10(4), Rob Latour p58(4), Lifestyle Graphic p119(tc), littlewormy p51(tr), Denis Makarenko p58(2), Oleksiy Mark p44(7), maicasaa p46(tr), MPH Photos p135(bl), Nerthuz p10(2), Netflix/Kobal/Beth Dubber p120(cr), Alena Ozerova p68(4), Prateek787 p49(cr), Rawpixel.com p76(tr), Yuri Shebalius p10(3), Sirinn3249 p129(bl), StarPix/Dave Allocca p58(6), stockphoto mania p17(tr), David Tadevosian p31(tl), T.Den_Team p144(6), Azat Valeev p105(d), Ewelina Walhalla p105(tl), suriya yapin p74(3), alis yimyen p52(cr), Vadym Zaitsev p52(5.1).

Video stills supplied by MTJ pp157, 158, 159, 160

The author and publishers are grateful for permission to reprint the following copyright material:
p141 Extract from 'Macmillan Readers, Little Women, Beginner Reader' © Anne Collins, 2005, reproduced with permission from Macmillan Education Limited. All rights reserved.
p143 Extract from 'Macmillan Readers, Adventures of Huckleberry Finn, Beginner Reader' © F.H. Cornish, 2005, reproduced with permission from Macmillan Education Limited. All rights reserved.
p145 Extract from 'Macmillan Readers, Northanger Abbey, Beginner Reader' © Florence Bell, 2005, reproduced with permission from Macmillan Education Limited. All rights reserved.

Additional sources:
p14 – Statistics from National Geographic Kids website, 2021; Moore, J.P. (2021) Peru, Britannica.com; easyscienceforkids.com website, 2021; sciencekids.co.nz website, 2021; WorldPopulationReview.com website, 2021.
p35 – A Day In The Life Of Climbing World Champion Sachia Amma (8 Jun 2018), YouTube.
p41 – 5 things you may not know about 15-year-old Coco Gauff (24 Jan 2020), Express & Star; Curtis, J. (2 July 2019) The parents who gave up everything for Wimbledon's newest star, MailOnline; Gauff unveils new hobbies and skills with Mattek-Sands (22 Apr 2020), Baseline.
p46 – Boyd, C. (10 Jan 2018) Speech Recognition Technology: The Past, Present, and Future, Medium.com; Rudgard, O. (31 Jan 2018) 'Alexa generation' may be learning bad manners from talking to digital assistants, report warns, The Telegraph; Top Voice Search Statistics, Facts And Trends For 2020 (27 Aug 2020), QuoraCreative.com; Donnelly, G. (20 Mar 2020), 33 Voice Search Statistics to Prepare You for the Voice Search Revolution, WordStream.com.
p62 – TIME's 25 Most Influential Teens of 2018 (7 Dec 2018), TIME; McGrath, M. (13 Jun 2017) From Activist To Author, Forbes.com.
p76 – Payne, R. (20 Jun 2016) What color room should you study in? MedicalXpress.com.
p129 – Statistics from LiveLighter.com.au, 2021; Zakharova, O. (2021), Obesity infographic; Lehnardt, K. (4 Oct 2019) 93 Interesting Junk Food Facts, FactRetriever.com; World Health Organization (15 Mar 2016) Fact Sheet: Adolescents' Dietary Habits.
p149 – Tetteh, S. (3 Mar 2019) Bright Spark, The Sun; Jackson, K. (6 Mar 2019) Einsteen, The Sun.

Printed and bound in Uruguay

2024
5

Contents

Starter What do you know?

Back to school

Vocabulary: saying hello

1 Complete the words with the missing letters.

1 T *h* *a* *n* *k* *s* .
2 I don't k ___ ___ ___ .
3 H ___ ___ are y ___ ___ ?
4 I'm f ___ ___ ___ .
5 T ___ ___ ___ ___ you.
6 G ___ ___ ___ b ___ ___ .
7 I'm n ___ ___ s ___ ___ ___ .

2 1 Order the sentences to make a conversation. Then listen and check.

a Bye. ___
b Hello Ben. How are you? *1*
c I'm not sure – err, Mr Cox. ___
d Hi Sarah. I'm OK, thanks, and you? ___
e Mr Cox is in Room 4. ___
f OK, thanks. Bye. ___
g I'm fine. Is this the English classroom? ___
h No, this is Mr Drake's Spanish class. Who is your English teacher this year? ___

Grammar: subject pronouns and possessive adjectives

3 Add the words in the box to the table.

he her his I it its my our she ~~their~~ they we you your

Subject pronouns	Possessive adjectives
	their

4 Write complete sentences with possessive adjectives.

1 I / Angus / phone
I'm Angus. It's my phone.
2 She / Kelly / chair
3 They / Marta and Chen / classroom
4 He / Oliver / bag
5 We / Aisha and Adara / school

5 Correct one mistake in sentences 1–7.

1 She's our new Spanish teacher. His name is Miss Gonzalez.
She's our new Spanish teacher. ***Her*** *name is Miss Gonzalez.*
2 I'm Eda and this is your friend Sevil. We're from Turkey.
3 **A:** Is this you pen? **B:** Oh yes, thanks.
4 That's the new boy in our class. He's from Ireland. He's name's Lester.
5 This is Meena and her friend Lara. Their in my English class.
6 **A:** I'm in class 7B. Is this our classroom?
B: No, this is 7A. You classroom is over there.
7 My friend Lola isn't in their class this year.

6 2 Complete the text with the words in the box. Then listen and check.

he I It My Our she We ~~your~~

Good morning everyone. Welcome to King's Park School. This is **1** *your* first day at King's Park. **2** ___ 's a big school so listen carefully. **3** ___ name's Mr Lenney and **4** ___ 'm the head of Year 7. This is Mrs Smart; **5** ___ 's a sports teacher. And this is Mr Gupta; **6** ___ is an English teacher. **7** ___ are your class teachers for classes 7A, 7B and 7C. **8** ___ classrooms are rooms 16, 17 and 18.

What's in your bag?

Vocabulary: personal objects

1 **Look at the pictures and complete the crossword.**

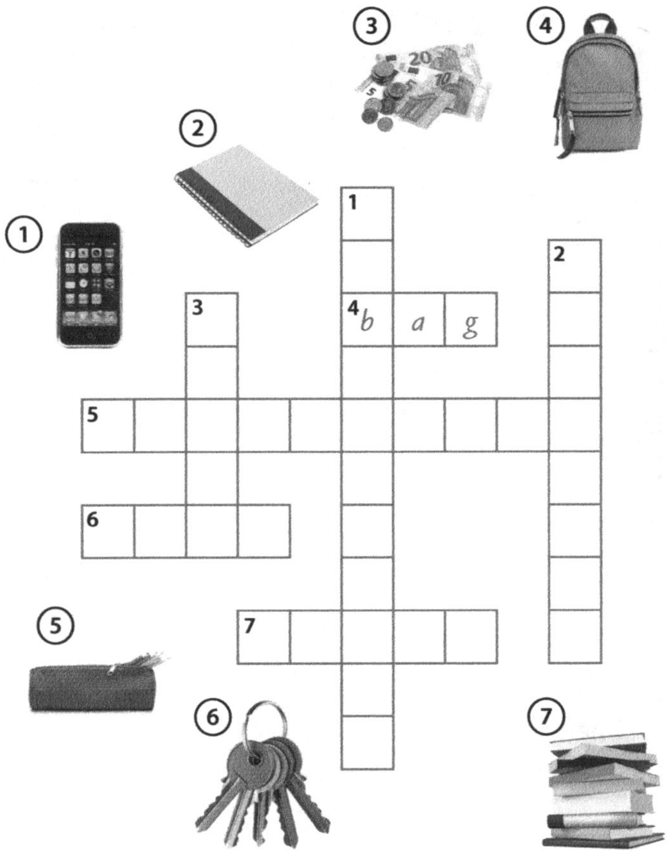

2 3 **What can you hear? Listen and choose the words from the box.**

~~books~~ keys mobile phone money pencil case

1 *books*
2 ______
3 ______
4 ______
5 ______

3 **Write a list of the things in your bag now. Then check to see if the list is correct.**

Mobile phone, ...

Grammar: *a*, *an* and plurals

4 **Complete with *a* or *an*.**

1 *a* pencil or ___ pen
2 ___ apple or ___ banana
3 ___ elephant or ___ rhino
4 ___ email or ___ phone number
5 ___ British pound or ___ American dollar
6 ___ computer or ___ mobile phone

5 **Look at the photos and write what you can see. Answer with vocabulary from exercise 4.**

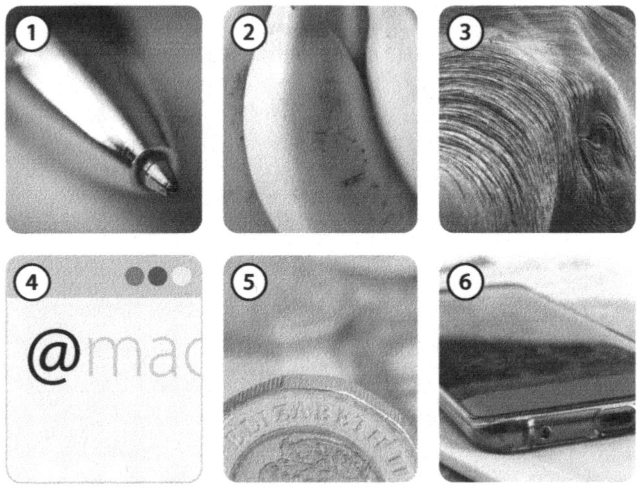

1 *a pen*
2 ______
3 ______
4 ______
5 ______
6 ______

6 **Complete the table with the words in the box. Use the plural form.**

box bus city class country dictionary key ~~party~~ school student

Most nouns	Nouns ending *-ch*, *-sh*, *-s*, *-ss* or *-x*	Nouns ending consonant *+y*
		parties

Grammar reference and practice pp82–83

Vocabulary: colours

7 **Correct the spelling of these colours.**

1 yelow *yellow*
2 broun ______
3 grean ______
4 wite ______
5 read ______
6 pinck ______
7 bleu ______
8 puple ______
9 blak ______

8 **Answer the quiz questions. You have three minutes!**

1 Which two colours mean Stop and Go?

______

2 If you mix blue and red, you get ______ .

3 The colours on the Mexican flag are

______ .

4 A flamingo is a ______ bird.

5 The most popular colour for mobile phones is

______ .

6 Hot chocolate and cola are ______ .

7 The Simpsons aren't black or white. They're

______ .

8 To get green, mix ______ and

______ .

9 Which colour completes all three expressions:

______ Friday, ______

market, ______ box.

10 The most popular colour for cars in the USA is

______ .

School days

Vocabulary: days of the week

1 **Write the complete word for the days of the week.**

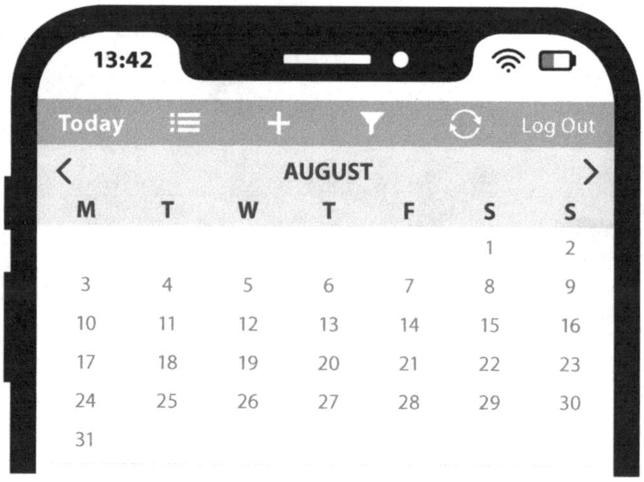

1 *Monday*
2 T______
3 W______
4 T______
5 F______
6 S______
7 S______

2 🔊4 **Listen and write the sentences you hear. Then correct the incorrect sentences.**

1 *The 3rd is a Tuesday.*
No, the 3rd is a Monday.
2 *The 14th is a Friday.*
That's right!
3 ______
4 ______
5 ______
6 ______
7 ______
8 ______

3 **Complete the text with the days of the week.**

A BUSY WEEKEND

The fourth **1** *Thursday* in November is a very special holiday in the USA. It's Thanksgiving when families eat a big lunch together. The next day is also important – for shopping! Black **2** ______ is the most important shopping day in the year. But now, it's not only a special day in the USA. In lots of countries, including Australia, Canada, Mexico and Spain, it's a special shopping day. But if you want a new computer or a mobile phone, wait until after Saturday and **3** ______ ! Cyber **4** ______ is the day to go shopping for a new mobile phone, laptop and other technology.

Vocabulary: the classroom

4 Complete the classroom objects with the missing vowels.

1 w *i* nd *o* w
2 p ___ st ___ r
3 cl ___ ck
4 c ___ mp ___ t ___ r
5 b ___ ___ rd
6 d ___ ___ r
7 ch ___ ___ r
8 d ___ sk

5 Look at the picture and write what you can see.

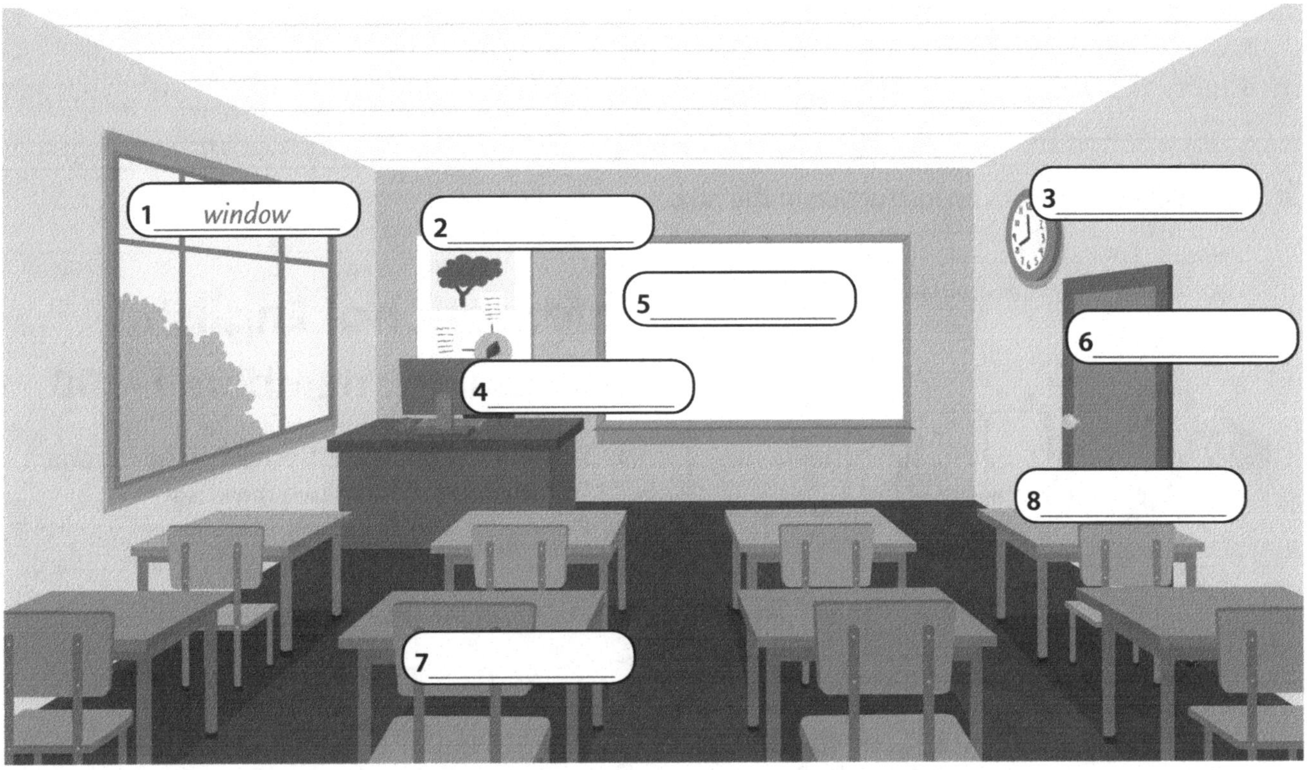

Grammar: *this, that, these, those*

6 Complete the table with *this, that, these, those.*

book	1 *this book*	5
keys	2	6
window	3	7
chairs	4	8

7 Choose the correct option.

1 **A:** Excuse me. Is **this/these** chair free?
B: Yes, **these are/that's** my chair with the green bag. This one is free.

2 **A:** Are **those/these** students over there in **this/these** class?
B: Yes, they're also in Class 7B.

3 **A:** Are **this/these** your books?
B: Yes, sorry. I'll move them.

4 **A:** Hi Tania. Who's **these/this** next to you?
B: Hello. **This/That** is Lois. It's her first day.
A: Hi Lois!

5 **A:** Are **these/this** your keys?
B: No, I think they're Danny's.
A: Who's Danny?
B: **This/That** boy next to the window, with the red bag.

Grammar reference and practice pp82–83

Instructions

Vocabulary: classroom instructions

1 Match the phrases to make instructions.

1	Look at	a	in pairs.
2	Work	b	the text.
3	Open your	c	your notebook.
4	Don't	d	the board.
5	Read	e	talk.
6	Copy this into	f	the answer.
7	Don't write	g	books at page 24.

2 Match each picture to an instruction in the box.

~~Listen.~~ Look at the board. Open your books. Work in pairs. Write your name.

① 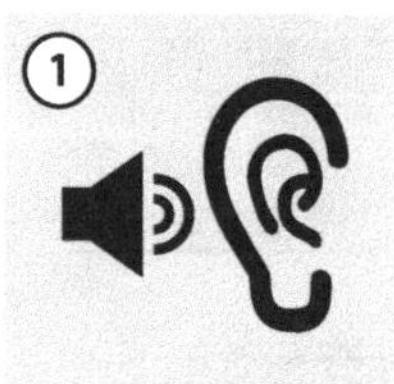

Listen.

② 

③ 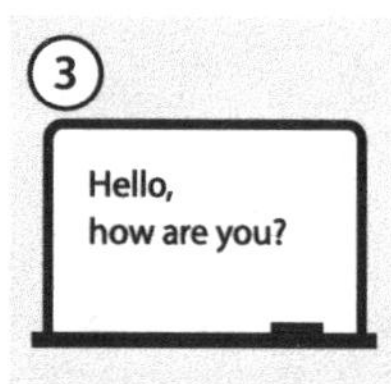

④ 

⑤ 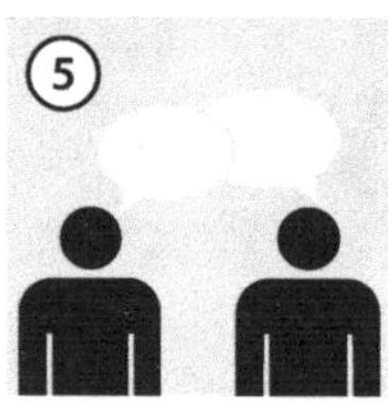

Grammar: imperatives

3 Rewrite the sentences and change affirmative to negative and negative to affirmative.

1 Read the text.
Don't read the text.

2 Don't work together.

3 Check your answers.

4 Write it in your notebook.

5 Open your books.

6 Don't read the text.

4 Order the words to make instructions.

1 at / look / me
Look at me.

2 write / don't / books / your / in

3 conversation / the / to / listen

4 in / of / work / groups / three

5 the / your / notebook / write / in / answers

6 your / check / pairs / in / answers

7 the / copy / questions / don't

International English

Vocabulary: numbers 1–100

1 Answer the quiz questions with the numbers in the box. You have two minutes!

12 ~~14~~ 28 37 42 44 52 55 62 77

BEAT THE CLOCK
Numbers Quiz!

1 The number of days in two weeks *14*
2 The number of days in July + May ___
3 The international telephone code for the UK 00 ___
4 The Roman numerals LV ___
5 The ideal temperature for the human body in °C (degrees centigrade) ___
6 The number of kilometres in a marathon ___
7 The number of days in February in a normal year ___
8 Find the answer: 52 + 36 – 11 ___
9 The number of months in a year ___
10 The number of weeks in a year ___

Vocabulary: international words

2 Use the alphabet code (A = 1, B = 2, etc.) to find five international words.

1 23 – 9 – 6 – 9
Wi-Fi
2 12 – 9 – 15 – 14
______
3 20 – 5 – 14 – 14 – 9 – 19
______
4 19 – 3 – 8 – 15 – 15 – 12
______
5 9 – 14 – 20 – 5 – 18 – 14 – 5 – 20
______

3 Read the clues and complete the words.

H *O T E L* You stay here on holiday.
H _ _ _ _ _ A sport
H _ _ _ _ _ _ _ You go here if you're ill.

P _ _ _ A place to go with friends on a nice day
P _ _ _ _ A popular Italian food
P _ _ _ _ A black and white animal from China
P _ _ _ _ Use this to call your friends.

C _ _ _ _ _ Use this to take photos.
C _ _ _ _ _ _ _ Dell, Asus and Mac are examples.
C _ _ _ _ _ _ _ _ This is brown and I love eating it!

4 Complete the table with the words from exercises 2 and 3.

Places	*hotel*
Technology	
Sports	
Animals	
Food	

Vocabulary: the alphabet

5 The letters in each column sound the same. Complete the table with the letters *D, K, M, S, T* and *U*.

1	2	3	4	5	6	7
A	B	F	I	O	Q	R
H	C	L	Y		W	
J	E	N			___	
___	G	X				
	P	Z				
	V	___				
	___	___				
	___					

6 🔊5 Listen and write the letters you hear to spell words.

1 g o __ __
2 __ __ __ __ __ __
3 __ __ __ __ __
4 __ __ __ __ __ __ __ __
5 __ __ __ __ __ __ __ __

7 Add the words in exercise 6 to the table in exercise 4.

1 Our world

Vocabulary

Countries and nationality adjectives

1 ☆ **Complete the countries and nationality adjectives with the missing letters.**

COUNTRIES

1 C *h* *i* n *a*
2 M ___ x ___ c ___
3 T ___ e U ___ ___ t ___ ___ S ___ ___ t ___ s
4 Sp ___ ___ ___

NATIONALITY ADJECTIVES

5 Am ___ ___ ___ c ___ n
6 B ___ ___ t ___ ___ h
7 Ch ___ ___ ___ s ___
8 ___ p ___ n ___ s ___
9 A ___ ___ ___ ra ___ i ___ n

2 ☆☆ **Write the missing sentences.**

1 It's from Mexico.
It's Mexican.

2 ______________
They're Dutch.

3 It's from India.
____

4 ______________
They're Turkish.

5 It's from Japan.
____

6 ______________
They're Brazilian.

7 They're from Russia.
____

8 ______________
It's Spanish.

3 ☆☆☆ **Complete the crossword and find the mystery word. Say a country in this place.**

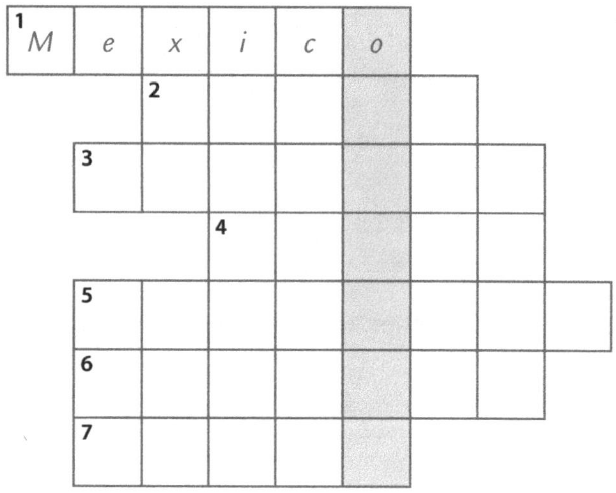

1 The name of the country is in the name of its capital city.
2 People from the Netherlands are ______________ .
3 Beijing is the ______________ capital city.
4 This country is between Portugal and France.
5 Sushi is a popular ______________ food.
6 Galatasaray is a ______________ football team from Istanbul.
7 Curry is a popular food in ______________ .

4 ☆☆☆ **Complete the sentences for you with countries or nationality adjectives.**

1 A country I would like to visit is ______________ because ______________
______________ .
2 I really like ______________ food. My favourite dish is ______________ .
3 I would like to try ______________ food.
4 I would like to watch sports in ______________ because ______________
______________ .
5 I think ______________ is a very beautiful country.

be: affirmative

1 ☆ **Complete the table with the words in the box.**

are It ~~'m~~ 's She They You

Subject pronoun	Full and contracted verb	
I	am 1 ___*'m*___	12 years old.
2 ______ We 4 ______	3 ______ 're	from Turkey.
He 5 ______ 7 ______	is 6 ______	a student.

2 ☆☆ **Complete what the ice skaters are saying. Use the contracted form of *be*.**

1 I'm Erin and he ___ Brad. We ___ from the United States.

2 They ___ from Russia. She ___ Olga and his name's Yuri.

3 We ___ the Canadian team.

4 Listen, it ___ the Russian national anthem!

3 ☆☆ **Choose the correct form of *be* to complete the text.**

Hi. I **1 is/'m** Bárbara and this **2 are/is** my sister Carla. She **3 's/'re** 15. We **4 am/'re** from Mexico. I **5 'm/m** in grade 7 and Carla's in grade 10. Our parents **6 is/are** Rosa and Bernardo. They **7 're/'s** both from Guadalajara. Dad's an English teacher at a school in Culiacán. Mum **8 's/s** a doctor at Médica Sur. It's a very big hospital here in Mexico City.

be: negative

4 ☆☆ **Look at the blocks and make sentences.**

I | Japanese | a doctor | My father | They | She | My friend | teachers | isn't | 'm not | You | aren't

1 *I'm not a doctor.*
2 ______
3 ______
4 ______
5 ______

5 ☆☆☆ 🔊6 **Listen to the sentences and rewrite them in the negative form.**

1 *They aren't from New Zealand.*
2 ______
3 ______
4 ______
5 ______
6 ______
7 ______

6 ☆☆☆ **Look at exercise 3. Write a similar description of yourself. Include three negative sentences using *be*.**

1 Vocabulary

Adjectives to describe places

1 ☆ **Complete the adjectives to describe places with the missing first letters.**

1 *u* gly
2 ___mpty
3 ___afe
4 ___lean
5 ___old
6 ___oring
7 ___odern
8 ___oisy

2 ☆☆ **Find the opposite of the adjectives in exercise 1 in the word square.**

A	B	B	C	D	E	F	J	D	N	O
I	N	T	E	R	E	S	T	I	N	G
G	Y	Z	L	A	M	H	K	R	I	J
H	K	L	M	Q	U	I	E	T	I	O
A	O	N	Q	U	O	T	P	Y	Q	L
B	C	T	R	S	U	V	I	T	X	D
C	R	O	W	D	E	D	F	F	G	H
U	V	D	A	N	G	E	R	O	U	S
P	R	S	D	E	T	W	W	X	Y	L

3 ☆☆ **Choose the correct option. Use the photos to help you.**

UNDERGROUND SYSTEMS AROUND THE WORLD

1 Don't travel alone on the New York subway at night. It isn't **safe/ dangerous**.
2 The metro stations in Moscow are very **ugly/ beautiful**.
3 In summer, trains on the London Underground are very **hot/cold**, with temperatures of more than 30°C.
4 In Japan, the metro is very **empty/crowded**.
5 In Madrid, there are new metro lines with very **old/modern** stations.
6 Visitors and local people love the metro in Hong Kong. They say it's very **clean/dirty**.

4 ☆☆☆ **Complete each paragraph with the adjectives in the boxes.**

cold hot

My city: Madrid

A time of year to visit

May. In summer, it's very **1** ______________ (35°C or more) and in winter, it's quite **2** ______________ (0–10°C), but in May, the weather is perfect.

boring modern

A place to go shopping

I like Islazul. It's a big, **3** ______________ shopping centre. And if you think shopping is **4** ______________ , it has lots of restaurants and cinemas, too.

crowded quiet empty

A place to relax

The centre of Madrid is sometimes very **5** ______________ with lots of people. El Capricho is a beautiful park in the north-east of the city. Lots of people visit at weekends, but on Mondays, it's **6** ______________ with no people. It's a good place to relax because it's very **7** ______________ .

5 ☆☆☆ **Write a city guide about a place you know.**

My city: ______________

A time of year to visit

____

____

A place to go shopping

____

____

A place to relax

____

____

be: questions and short answers

1 ☆ **Choose the correct option.**

1 Are …
  (a) they from our school?
  b he Mexican?
2 Am …
  a you from the United States?
  b I in this class?
3 Is …
  a this your phone?
  b these your books?
4 Are …
  a your city modern?
  b the parks in your city beautiful?
5 Is …
  a New Orleans an expensive city?
  b the shops crowded on Mondays?

2 ☆☆ **Complete the other questions in exercise 1 with the correct form of *be*.**

1 *b Is he Mexican?*
2 ______
3 ______
4 ______
5 ______

3 ☆☆ 🔊7 **Order the sentences to make a conversation. Use the short answers to help you. Then listen and check.**

a **Keira:** No, I'm not. I'm from Ireland. Fabio – that's not an English name. ___
b **Keira:** Yes, I am. My name's Keira. ___
c **Fabio:** Yes, they are! They're from Milan. ___
d **Fabio:** Hi. I'm Fabio. Where are you from, Keira? Are you English? ___
e **Keira:** Wait – are they Italian? ___
f **Fabio:** No, it isn't. I'm from England, but my mum and dad … ___
g **Fabio:** Hi. Are you new in this school? *1*

4 ☆☆ **Write true answers for the questions.**

1 Are the beaches in Auckland crowded?
  No, they aren't.
2 Is New York a quiet city?
  ______
3 Are Ankara and Istanbul in Turkey?
  ______
4 Is Sydney the capital of Australia?
  ______
5 Are you English?
  ______
6 Is Portuguese the language of Brazil?
  ______
7 Are you and your friends students of English?
  ______

5 ☆☆☆ **Write complete questions. Then write answers for you.**

1 your city / modern ?
  Is your city modern? Yes, it is.
2 the transport system in your city / old ?
  ______
3 parts of your city / dangerous ?
  ______
4 your mother and father / from the same city ?
  ______
5 your city / the capital city of your country ?
  ______
6 you and your best friend / from the same part of the city ?
  ______

Grammar reference and practice pp84–85

1 Reading

A guidebook

Focus on ... PERU

City Life

Seventy percent of Peruvians live in cities. Eight million people live in the capital, Lima. It's a great place to visit with beautiful beaches, fantastic restaurants and interesting museums. Other important cities are Arequipa and Callao.

Geography

Peru is a big country in South America and it's a very beautiful country with mountains and beaches. Its neighbours are Ecuador, Colombia, Brazil, Bolivia and Chile. The most important mountains are the Andes. Two important rivers are the Amazon and the Ucayali. Ubinas is an active volcano!

Country Fact File

Name: Republic of Peru
Nationality: Peruvian
Capital City: Lima
Population: 32.9 million
Official languages: Spanish, Quechua and Aymara
Currency: Sol (pl. soles)

Places to visit

See the Inca city at Machu Picchu.
Visit the pyramids at Pachacamac near Lima.
Go to beautiful Huascaran National Park.
Peru is a great place for all kinds of adventure sports.

fun facts In just one square kilometre of Peruvian rainforest there are 6,000 different types of plant.

1 ☆ **Think about what you know about Peru. Which three things are true?**

1 It's a country in South America. *True*
2 People in Peru speak Portuguese. ______
3 Its capital city is Lima. ______
4 Peru was home to the Inca people. ______

▶ Subskill: Identifying different types of text

Look at the text before you read. Think about what type of information is in the text.

2 ☆☆ **Before you read, look at the different parts of the article. Do you think it includes …**

1 basic information about the country (cities, language, currency, etc.).
2 information about the most important football teams.
3 information about the natural world.
4 useful language and expressions for visitors.
5 ideas for visitors to the country.
6 information about prices and how much things cost.

3 ☆☆ 🔊8 **Read and listen to the article and check your ideas in exercise 2.**

4 ☆☆ **Answer the questions.**

1 How many people live in Peru?
32.9 million
2 Do Peruvian people pay in euros?
______
3 What percentage (%) of Peruvians live in cities?
______
4 Is Ucayali a city in Peru?
______
5 Why is Ubinas sometimes a dangerous place?
______
6 What can I see at Pachacamac?
______

5 ☆☆☆ **Which section would you include the following information in?**

1 Area: 1.3 million kilometres
Country Fact File
2 Trujillo is another important Peruvian city.
______
3 The Sechura and the Atacama are two deserts.
______
4 National Holidays: 28th and 29th July
______
5 Go by plane to see the Nazca Lines.
______

6 ☆☆☆ **What would you most like to do in Peru? Why?**

A podcast

Subskill: Using visual clues

Look at headings, photos and maps to get information before you listen.

1 ☆ Look at the photos. Which things do you think the podcast talks about?

1 The most important cities in the USA
2 A great place for teens to live in the USA
3 A fun activity at a park
4 Popular sports for American teenagers
5 A robotics camp

2 ☆☆ 🔊9 Listen to the podcast and check your answers in exercise 1.

3 ☆☆☆ Listen again. Choose the correct option.

1 Irvine is in the state of **Texas/California**
2 Parents like Irvine because it's a **safe/modern** city.
3 Irvine has great **schools/weather**.
4 In Orange County Great Park, you can **do sports/go shopping**.
5 Irvine Spectrum Center has some excellent **sports facilities/restaurants**.
6 At Beall Center for Art and Technology, they have a summer program on **making films/robotics**.

Meeting new people

1 ☆ Complete the phrases with the words in the box.

11	from	I'm	~~name~~	Nice	old

1 What's your *name* ?
2 ______ to meet you.
3 Where are you ______ ?
4 How ______ are you?
5 ______ Josh.
6 I'm ______ .

2 ☆☆ Order the sentences to make a conversation.

A: Me too! ___
A: Hi. I'm Kerry. What's your name? *1*
A: You too. Where are you from, Freya? ___
A: I'm from England. How old are you? ___
B: I'm from Nigeria. And you? ___
B: I'm 12. ___
B: I'm Freya. Nice to meet you. ___

3 ☆☆☆ Complete the conversation with appropriate expressions.

Hello, I'm Zoe.
1 ______ ?

2 ______ ,
Zoe. I'm Freddy.

Nice to meet you Freddy.
3 ______ ?

I'm 11.
4 ______ ?

I'm 12.

Where 5 ______ ?

6 ______
Edinburgh, in Scotland.

1 Writing

A keypal message

1 ☆ **Match the examples in the box with rules 1–5.**

Dutch I'm 12 ~~Japan~~ Washington D.C. Wednesday

Use a capital letter for …

1 countries *Japan*
2 nationalities and languages ______
3 cities ______
4 days of the week ______
5 the pronoun 'I' ______

2 ☆☆ **Write *S* if you use the expression to start a message, *W* if you say why you want a keypal and *A* if you ask someone to write to you.**

1 Send me a message. *A*
2 Hi! ___
3 I want to know more about other countries. ___
4 Please write to me. ___
5 Hi there! ___
6 I want to make new friends. ___

3 ☆☆☆ **Think of a famous person. Write to them and ask them to be your keypal.**

To: Marc Márquez From: Pablo

Hi Marc!
My name's Pablo. I'm from Caracas, the capital of Venezuela …

Super skills

COLLABORATION

SUPER SKILLS

It's important to use your imagination to think of creative ideas.

Tick (✔) the expressions that show you like an idea.

I like that idea. ☐
It's not very original. ☐
That's great! ☐
Let's think of more ideas before we decide. ☐
Mmm OK, but what about … ? ☐
That's really different. Good idea! ☐

Vocabulary review

Countries and nationality adjectives

1 Complete the table with the countries and nationality adjectives in the box.

Brazil Chinese Indian Japan Mexican Spanish the Netherlands ~~the UK~~ the USA

	Countries	Nationality adjectives
Europe	1 *the UK* 2	3
Asia	4	5 6
America	7	8

Adjectives to describe places

2 Complete the missing adjectives.

1 The park is very b*eautiful* with lots of trees and a river.
2 Amsterdam is a very cool city with lots of i______ places to visit.
3 My grandparents' village is very q______ and there's nothing to do. It's a bit b______.
4 My friends' school is very m______ with a robotics lab and a new sports centre, but it's quite u______.

3 Match 1–5 with a–e to make sentences.

1 The weather's terrible. It's too hot in summer — d
2 Most parts of the city are very safe, but at night
3 I want some clean clothes. My T-shirt
4 It's very noisy here. I can't study. Let's go
5 On a Monday, the shopping centre is empty, but

a is very dirty after my run in the park.
b the old part is a bit dangerous.
c at weekends it's very crowded.
d and too cold in winter.
e to the library. It's quiet in there.

Grammar review

be: affirmative and negative

1 Complete the text with the correct form of the verb *be*. Use contracted forms where possible.

I **1** _*'m*_ **(+)** American, but my parents **2** ________ **(+)** from Costa Rica. It **3** ________ **(+)** a small country, but it's on both the Pacific and Atlantic Oceans, so you **4** ________ **(–)** more than two hours from the beach. My family **5** ________ **(–)** from the capital, San Jose. We **6** ________ **(+)** from Puerto Viejo. I love it there! It **7** ________ **(–)** big or crowded, but it **8** ________ **(+)** very beautiful. I **9** ________ **(+)** always happy in Puerto Viejo!

be: questions and short answers

2 Complete the dialogue with questions and short answers.

Beth: Hi. I'm Mimi. **1** your name/Beth?
*Is your name Beth?*

Mimi: **2** (✔) _*Yes, it is.*_

Beth: The teacher says you're from Ireland. **3** you/from Dublin? ________________

Mimi: **4** (✘) ________________
I'm from Galway.

Beth: Where's Galway? **5** it/in the east?
____

Mimi: **6** (✘) ________________
It's in the west of Ireland.

Beth: **7** your parents/from Galway, too?
____

Mimi: **8** (✘) ________________
My dad's from Cork and my mum's from Waterford.

Round-up 1 2 3 4 5 6 7 8

Choose the correct option.

INTERNATIONAL ENGLISH

1 You are/Are you a student of English? Are you 13 or more? A visit to an English-speaking country **2 be/is** a fantastic way to learn. This week we talk to two high school students from Korea.

Q & A (Question and Answer)

Q Hi. What are your names?

A I **3 's/'m** Rose and this **4 is/'s** Ha-Yoon. We **5 're/'s** from Seoul, but this year we **6 aren't/isn't** in Korea. Ha-Yoon and I **7 'm/are** at school in Auckland, New Zealand.

Q **8 Are you/You are** happy in Auckland?

A Yes, **9 I am/I'm**. New Zealand is very beautiful.

Q What about the school? **10 Is it/It's** very different from Korea?

A Yes, **11 it isn't/it is.** We study different things.

Q Are you here for the full school year?

A No, we **12 aren't/isn't**. I'm here for three months and Ha-Yoon **13 are/is** here for six.

Self-evaluation

Read the objectives for this unit. How well can you now do each one? Put a tick (✔).

	😀	😐	🙁
1 I can talk about countries and nationalities.	☐	☐	☐
2 I can use the verb *be*.	☐	☐	☐
3 I can use adjectives to describe places.	☐	☐	☐
4 I can identify different types of text.	☐	☐	☐
5 I can use visual clues.	☐	☐	☐
6 I can use my imagination.	☐	☐	☐
7 I can write a keypal message.	☐	☐	☐

If you choose 🙁, ask your teacher for some extra help.

Grammar reference and practice pp84–85

2 Family

Vocabulary

Family; describing people

1 ☆ **Complete the descriptions of these famous families with words in the box. Check online if you don't know.**

brothers	children	cousin
daughter	~~father~~	sister	son

In the *Harry Potter* series,

1 Arthur Weasley is Ron's ___*father*___ .
2 George and Fred are Ron's ________ .
3 Dudley is Harry's ________ .

In *The Hunger Games*,

4 Primrose Everdeen is Katniss's ________ .
5 Katniss and Primrose are Mrs Everdeen's ________ .

In *The Lion King*,

6 Nala is Sarafina's ________ .
7 Simba is Mufasa's ________ .

2 ☆☆ **Match 1–6 with a–f.**

1 He's my nephew. — b
2 She's my daughter.
3 They're our children.
4 She's my granddaughter.
5 He's my uncle.
6 She's my grandmother.

a He's my grandfather.
b She's my aunt.
c He's my grandson.
d She's my mother.
e They're our parents.
f She's my niece.

3 ☆☆ **Complete the adjectives with the missing letters.**

1 o *l* d
2 t _ _ l
3 d _ _ k
4 s _ _ _ t
5 y _ _ _ g
6 f _ _ r

4 ☆☆ **Put the adjectives in exercise 3 in pairs of opposites.**

1 ________________
2 ________________
3 ________________

5 ☆☆ **Complete the descriptions with the adjectives from exercise 3.**

I can see two people. On the right, I can see a boy. He's not very **1** ___*young*___ . He's about 12 years old. He's with a woman. I'm not sure who she is. Maybe she's his grandmother, but she's not very **2** ________ . I think she's his aunt. The woman has got **3** ________ hair, but the boy's hair is **4** ________ . I don't know if they're **5** ________ or short from this photo.

6 ☆☆☆ **Write descriptions of three people in your family.**

1 ________________
____
2 ________________
____
3 ________________
____

have got: affirmative and negative

1 ☆ **Rewrite the sentences and change affirmative to negative and negative to affirmative. Use contractions.**

1 I've got a cousin in the United States.
I haven't got a cousin in the United States.
2 My uncle and aunt haven't got children.
______
3 My grandmother's got a sister called Lucy.
______
4 My best friend hasn't got brothers and sisters.
______
5 My sister and I have got a French grandfather.
______
6 I've got a three-year-old nephew.
______
7 You haven't got a sister.
______

2 ☆☆ **Write all the possible sentences using the affirmative or negative forms of *have/has got* and contractions where possible.**

I My best friend My uncle and aunt	a house in Texas. two dogs.

My best friend has got a house in Texas.
______
______

3 ☆☆ **Complete the text with the correct form of *have got*.**

Liam and Chris Hemsworth are Australian actors. The brothers **1** *have got* **(+)** blue eyes. *Hunger Games* star, Liam, **2** ______ **(+)** dark hair, but Chris, who stars in the *Thor* films, **3** ______ **(+)** fair hair. Chris and Liam **4** ______ **(+)** an older brother, Luke, but they **5** ______ **(–)** any sisters. Chris and his wife, Spanish actress Elsa Pataky, **6** ______ **(+)** three children. Liam **7** ______ **(–)** any children.

Possessive *'s*

4 ☆ **Choose the correct option.**

1 That's my **grandparent's/grandparents'** car.
2 This is my **brother's/brothers'** phone.
3 These are my cousins. My **cousins'/cousin's** mum is a doctor.
4 Look! That's **Lisa's/Lisas'** father.
5 These are my **mothers'/mother's** friends, Ellie and Max.
6 My **parents'/parent's** favourite restaurant is in San Sebastian.

5 ☆☆ **Complete the sentences with possessive nouns.**

1 That's my *grandmother's* car. **(grandmother)**
2 Their ______ name is Jane. **(daughter)**
3 My ______ names are Scott and Jamie. **(cousin)**
4 My ______ mum is called Lily. **(best friend)**
5 The ______ uncle is in Florida. **(children)**
6 This is my ______ bag. **(father)**

6 ☆☆☆ **Write sentences about your family.**

1 ______ cousins.
2 My mother ______.
3 My father's ______.
4 ______ brothers.

Parts of the body; describing face and hair

1 ☆ **Complete the crossword with parts of the body.**

Across

2 

4 

6 

7 

8 

9 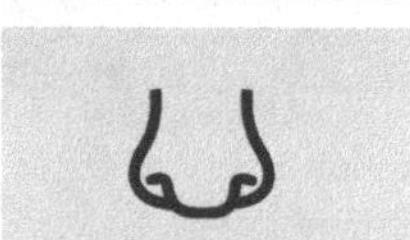

10 

Down

1 

3 

5 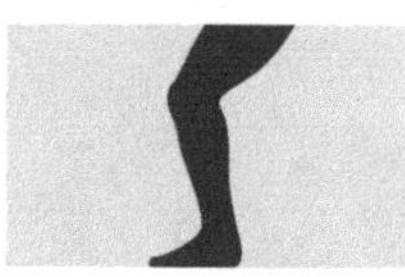

6 

8 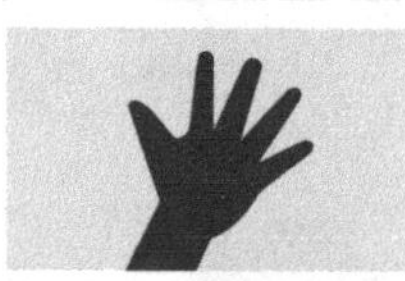

11 

2 ☆☆ **Complete the sentences with parts of the body. Use the plural form where necessary.**

1 My brother's got big *feet*. He's a size 46.
2 I've got green ______, but my sister's are blue.
3 Please close your ______ when you eat!
4 Raise your ______ if you can answer the question.
5 Look! The baby has got his first ______!
6 Insects have got six ______.
7 Dad hasn't got any ______ on his head, but he's got a ______ and a long ______ on his face.

3 ☆☆ **Read the descriptions and identify the people in the photo. There are two extra people.**

1 Pia's got dark eyes. Her hair is dark brown. It's long and straight. *E*
2 Jackson has got short, black hair. His hair is straight. ___
3 Shania's got long, brown hair and blue eyes. ___
4 Kieran has got very short, curly hair and brown eyes. ___

4 ☆☆☆ **Write descriptions of the two other people in the photograph.**

1 ______________________
____
____

2 ______________________
____
____

have got: questions and short answers

1 ☆ **Choose the correct option.**

1 **Have/Has** you got a sister?
2 **Have/Has** your cousin got a moustache?
3 Has **your teacher/your uncles** got a beard?
4 **Has/Have** your parents got blue eyes?
5 Have **your best friend/you** got long hair?
6 **Has/Have** I got curly hair?

2 ☆☆ **Write questions with *have got* and *a/an* or *any*. Then write a short answer for you.**

All about you

1 cousins
Have you got any cousins?

2 mobile phone
______

3 favourite singer
______

4 friends in other countries
______

5 unusual hobby
______

3 ☆☆ **Correct one mistake in each question.**

1 Have your friend got any sisters?
Has your friend got any sisters?
2 Has your grandparents got a house near the sea?
______
3 Have you got any black schoolbag?
______
4 Has you brother got a musical instrument?
______
5 Has your teacher got a children?
______
6 Have your parent got a new car?
______

4 ☆☆ **Read the information about a film. Then match questions 1–6 with answers a–f.**

The Addams Family is an animated film with the following characters:

Gomez Addams and his wife, Morticia; their daughter, Wednesday, and son, Pugsley; Gomez's brother, Uncle Fester; Gomez and Fester's mother, Grandmama.

Two of the actors in the film are Chloë Grace Moretz as Wednesday, and Finn Wolfhard as Pugsley.

1 Have Morticia and Gomez got a daughter? — b
2 Has Wednesday got a brother?
3 'Gomez, have you got a sister?'
4 Has Pugsley got a brother?
5 'Wednesday and Pugsley, have you got an uncle?'
6 'Grandmama, have you got a granddaughter?'

a No, he hasn't.
b Yes, they have.
c Yes, I have.
d Yes, she has.
e Yes, we have.
f No, I haven't.

5 ☆☆☆ **Think of a character in a film you like and answer the questions.**

Character's name: ______

1 Has he/she got any brothers or sisters?
______
2 Has he/she got any special abilities?
______
3 Has he/she got any pets?
______
4 Has he/she got any special friends?
______

A book recommendation

fun facts We all know about YouTubers, but do you know about BookTubers? BookTubers give book recommendations online!

My book recommendation

My favourite book is *The Rest of the Story* by Sarah Dessen. It's the story of a girl called Emma Saylor. Her mother, Waverly, is dead and Emma lives in the city with her father, Matthew, who is a dentist. The family are quite rich. Emma doesn't know her mother's family, but when her father gets married again, she goes to spend the summer where they live, at North Lake. She meets her cousins and her grandmother, Mimi, and she works with them in the family business, a small hotel. At the lake, some people are rich, but others, like her mother's family, aren't rich. Emma makes friends with a boy called Roo and learns secrets* about her mother and father. This helps her understand who she is.

This is a story about families and love, and it's a great book for the summer holidays. Sarah Dessen understands teenagers very well and I like all her books. I recommend you read it!

*information that most people don't know

recommendation (n.)

when you tell other people that something (a film, a book, a restaurant) is good

Subskill: Predicting what a text is about

Pictures can help you understand a text. Look at them before you read.

1 ☆ **Before you read, look at the photo and choose the correct option. Do you think the book is about … ?**

a summer or winter
b the city or the country
c people or technology
d a crowded place or a quiet place

2 ☆☆ 🔊 10 **Read the definition. Then read and listen to a book recommendation and check your answers in exercise 1.**

3 ☆☆ **Who are the people? Read and complete the information with words in the box.**

a boy Emma meets	Emma's father	Emma's mother	~~the most important character~~	the writer of the book	Waverly's mother and Emma's grandmother

Name	Who are they?
Emma	*the most important character*
Matthew	
Waverly	
Mimi	
Roo	
Sarah	

4 ☆☆☆ **Are the sentences T (true) or F (false)? Correct the false sentences.**

1 Emma lives with her mother. ________
2 Emma's father is a doctor. ________
3 Her father's family is rich. ________
4 Her mother's family have got a shop. ________
5 Her mother's family are rich. ________
6 Emma learns new things about her family. ________
7 This is a good book to read on holiday. ________
8 This is the only book by Sarah Dessen. ________

5 ☆☆☆ **Do you want to read this book? Why/Why not?**

____

Playing a game with friends

Subskill: Using what you know

Think what you know about the topic before you listen.

1 ☆ **Look at the photos and answer the questions.**

A

B

1 The people have papers on their heads in Photo A. Can they see the writing on the paper on their own head?

a Yes b No

2 Is the girl in Photo B …

a one of the friends. b a famous person.

2 ☆☆ 11 **Listen to the friends playing the game and tick (✔) the questions Gemma asks.**

1 Am I a man? ✔
2 Have I got long hair? ☐
3 What's my job? ☐
4 Am I American? ☐
5 Am I an actor? ☐
6 Am I good at sport? ☐
7 Am I a football player? ☐
8 Am I a gymnast? ☐
9 Am I short? ☐
10 Am I Simone Biles? ☐

3 ☆☆☆ **Tick (✔) the two problems in the game.**

1 Alex can't think of a famous person to write. ☐
2 Gemma asks the wrong type of question. ☐
3 Gemma sees the name on her paper. ☐
4 Alex and Neesha don't know the answer to one of the questions. ☐

Talking about photos

1 ☆ **Write A (asking about a photo), T (talking about people in a photo) or O (giving an opinion).**

1 This is his friend. *T*
2 Who's this? ___
3 That's really nice. ___
4 How old is he? ___
5 That's our cousin. ___
6 This is a great photo. ___
7 Where are they? ___

2 ☆☆ **Complete the dialogue with the phrases in exercise 1.**

1 *This is a great photo.*

Thanks.

2 ___________________________?

It's my brother Sam and 3 ___________________________, Marshall. His dad is my mum's brother.

4 ___________________________?

He's 13. Look, 5 ___________________________, Lea.

6 ___________________________?

At Lea's birthday party.

7 ___________________________.

2 Writing

An email

1 ☆ **Choose the correct answer.**

1 **a** This is my sisters book.
  (b) This is my sister's book.
2 **a** He is my brother.
  b Hes my brother.
3 **a** That's my father's car.
  b That's my fathers car.

2 ☆☆ **What is the *'s* in the underlined words? Write *is, has* or *P* (for possession).**

1 **A:** Joanne's got my phone. Where is she? *has*
  B: She's in the computer room. ______
2 **A:** Is this Karina's bag? ______
  B: No, she's got a green bag. ______
3 **A:** That's a nice photo. ______
  B: Yes, it's my sister's birthday. ______

3 ☆☆ **Complete the text with the missing apostrophes.**

It's Bens birthday today. Hes 12 and hes got a party after school. The partys in his mothers restaurant. Shes a cook. The restaurants in the centre of town and its got a big room for parties.

4 ☆☆☆ **It's your birthday! Write an email to tell a friend about your plans.**

Super skills

COLLABORATION

SUPER SKILLS

Be open; it's a good idea to think about things in different ways.

Match 1–4 with a–d to make expressions.

1 What about — d
2 Have you got
3 Football isn't
4 Is football important to

a any more ideas?
b all the students?
c the only option.
d other sports?

2

Vocabulary review

Family

1 **Look at the family tree and complete the sentences about people in the family.**

1 Julia is Mark's *mother* .
2 Finn is *Lola's* brother.
3 Lola is Finn's ______ .
4 Dennis is Laura's ______ .
5 ______ is Dennis and Julia's daughter.
6 Mark is Finn and Lola's ______ .
7 Finn is ______ grandson.
8 Lola is Mark's ______ .

Describing people

2 **Complete the table with the words in the box.**

arm ~~curly~~ ear eye foot hand leg long mouth nose old short short straight tall teeth young

Describing hair	*curly*
Parts of the head	
Parts of the body	
Describing a person	

3 **Complete the description.**

My uncle Steven is my mum's brother. Mum and Steven have both got dark hair and blue **1** ______ , but in other ways, they're very different. He's **2** ______ – about 2 metres, and she's quite **3** ______ – only about 1m 55. Mum's hair is long and straight, but Steven's hair is the opposite: it's **4** ______ and **5** ______ .

Grammar review

have got: affirmative and negative

1 Complete the sentences with the correct form of *have got*.

1 Sophie **(+)** _*'s got*_ two brothers.
2 My cousins love animals. They **(+)** ______ two dogs and three cats.
3 I **(–)** ______ any brothers and sisters.
4 Nina can't open the door. She **(–)** ______ a key.
5 We **(–)** ______ a big house.
6 **A:** Are you OK?
B: No, I'm not. I **(+)** ______ something in my eye.

Possessive *'s*

2 Write the apostrophe(s) in the correct position.

1 My sister*'*s favourite colour is blue.
2 Is this your grandparents house?
3 My friends names are Paula and Carmen.
4 Have you got Jeremys phone number?
5 My brothers friends name is Lottie.
6 The childrens parents are in Paris this weekend.

have got: questions and short answers

3 Write complete questions with *a/an/any* + *have got*.

1 you / brothers and sisters ?
Have you got any brothers or sisters?
2 you / favourite song ?
______
3 your best friend / pets ?
______
4 your parents / favourite restaurant ?
______
5 your classroom / computers ?
______
6 you / aunt ?
______
7 your city / airport ?
______
8 your teacher / beard ?
______

Round-up 1 2 3 4 5 6 7 8

Choose the correct option.

The world's favourite cartoon family

Which is the **1 world's/worlds'** favourite cartoon family? **2 It is/Is it** the Flintstones or the Griffins from *Family Guy*? No, it **3 not/isn't**. You **4 's/'re** wrong. **5 Is/It's** the most famous yellow family on TV: the Simpsons! Homer and Marge Simpson **6 have got/has got** three children: ten-year-old Bart and his **7 sister's/sisters** Lisa and Maggie. The **8 Simpson's/Simpsons'** home is in Springfield in the USA. Homer works, but Marge **9 hasn't/isn't** got a job. **10 Have got the Simpsons/Have the Simpsons got** a perfect life? No, they **11 hasn't/haven't**. They **12 re/'re** not your typical American family.

Self-evaluation

Read the objectives for this unit. How well can you now do each one? Put a tick (✔).

	😀	😐	🙁
1 I can talk about different people in a family.	☐	☐	☐
2 I can describe the body and people's appearance.	☐	☐	☐
3 I can use *have got* and possessive *'s*.	☐	☐	☐
4 I can predict information before I read using pictures.	☐	☐	☐
5 I can use what I know about a topic before I listen.	☐	☐	☐
6 I can talk about photos.	☐	☐	☐
7 I can write an email.	☐	☐	☐

If you choose 🙁, ask your teacher for some extra help.

Grammar reference and practice pp86–87

3 Eat well

Vocabulary

Food and drink

1 ☆ **Look at the photos and write the words in the box.**

banana ~~bread~~ cheese chocolate coffee fish potato tomato water

1 *bread*

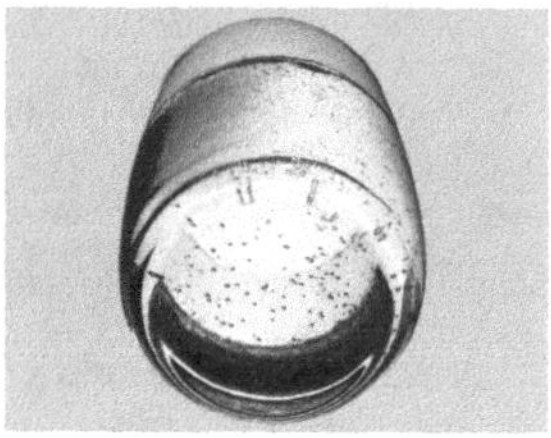

2 ______

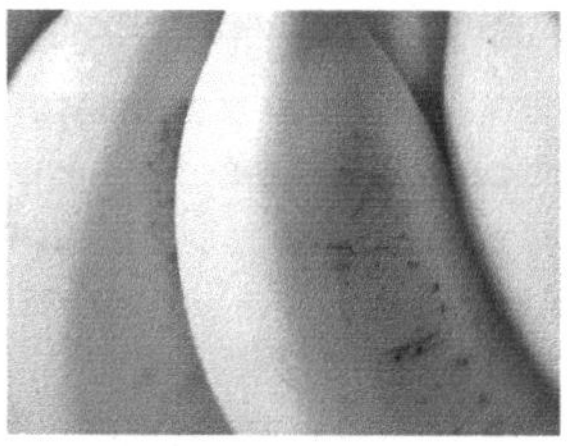

3 ______

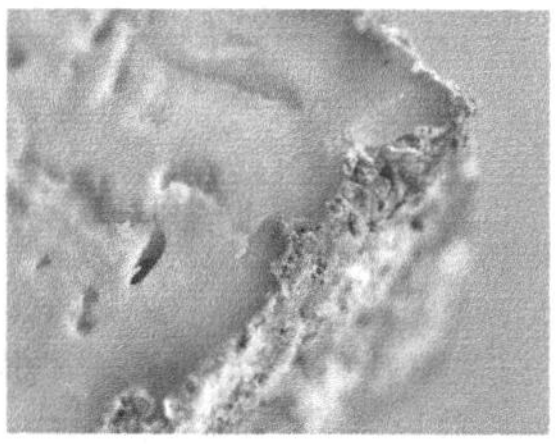

4 ______

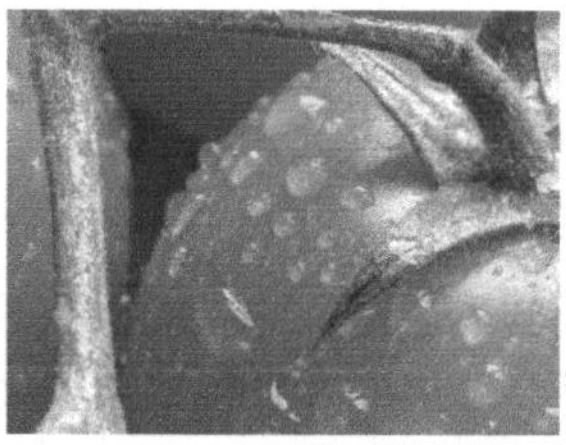

5 ______

6 ______

7 ______

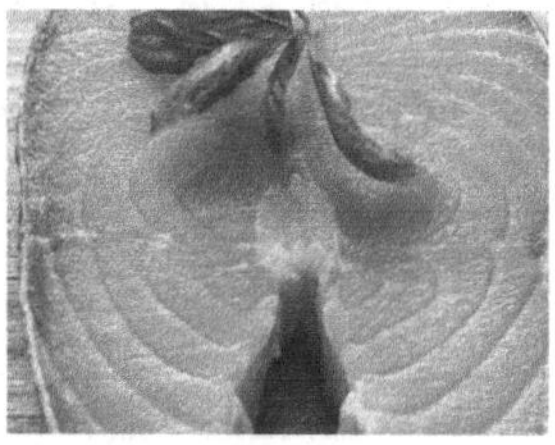

8 ______

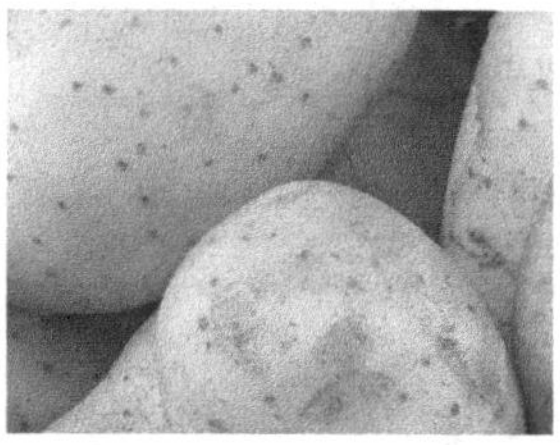

9 ______

2 ☆☆ **Complete the food and drink words with the missing first letters.**

1 *c* hicken
2 ___iscuit
3 ___ea
4 ___uice
5 ___il
6 ___ice
7 ___pple
8 ___andwich
9 ___eas
10 ___eat
11 ___range
12 ___oup

3 ☆☆ **Complete the table with the words in the box.**

apple biscuit cheese chocolate ~~coffee~~ fish juice orange peas potato rice sandwich soup tea water

drinks	*coffee*
fruit and vegetables	
sweet things	
other food	

4 ☆☆ **Choose the correct option.**

1 My best friend's a vegetarian. She doesn't eat any **bread/meat**.
2 When we go for a picnic we normally take some **sandwiches/peas**.
3 It's important to drink lots of **coffee/water** when you do sport.
4 I'd like a cup of tea and **some rice/a biscuit**, please.
5 **A:** What type of soup is it?
B: Tomato/Banana.
6 What type of **tea/juice** would you like? Orange or apple?
7 Would you like some rice with your **apples/chicken**?

5 ☆☆☆ **What do you like to eat and drink … ?**

1 after doing sport

______

2 at a party

______

3 for breakfast

______

Countable and uncountable nouns

1 ☆ **Write C (countable) or U (uncountable) next to the words.**

1	apple	*C*	8	key	___
2	class	___	9	money	___
3	juice	___	10	pasta	___
4	computer	___	11	rice	___
5	dollar	___	12	sandwich	___
6	homework	___	13	water	___
7	hotel	___			

2 ☆☆ **Match 1–6 with a–f to make sentences.**

1	I've got an	a	tomatoes, please?
2	Have you got a	b	orange.
3	After sport, eat a	c	money in my bag.
4	Can I have an	d	banana.
5	I've got some	e	apple?
6	Can I have some	f	black pen?

3 ☆☆ **Complete the dialogue with *a, an* or *some*.**

A: Next?

B: What's for lunch today?

A: We've got **1** ___*a*___ cheese and tomato pizza and I've got **2** ______ fish with potatoes. Oh, and pasta.

B: OK – I'd like **3** ______ pasta, please. What about fruit?

A: What would you like? **4** ______ apple? **5** ______ banana?

B: No fruit, thanks.

A: And to drink?

B: I'd like **6** ______ juice, please.

some, any, a lot of

4 ☆☆ **Which sentences are correct? Correct the incorrect sentences.**

1 We haven't got some coffee.
We haven't got any coffee.

2 They've got a lot of chicken.
______

3 We've got a lot students in our class.
______

4 Have you got any homework today?
______

5 We haven't got any Wi-Fi in this hotel.
______

6 My father hasn't got some keys for the car.
______

5 ☆☆ **Write complete sentences to describe the picture with *some, any* and *a lot of*.**

1 apples
We've got a lot of apples.

2 bread
______

3 biscuits
______

4 cheese
______

5 fish
______

6 juice
______

7 tomatoes
______

6 ☆☆☆ **Write what you have usually got in your fridge at home.**

______
______
______
______

The shopping centre

1 ☆ **Find four names of places you can buy food in the word square.**

F	A	U	E	C	U	T	Y	D	B	M
O	R	E	S	T	A	U	R	A	N	T
O	L	I	H	H	N	F	U	O	O	C
D	A	P	Q	R	S	B	E	V	P	L
S	U	P	E	R	M	A	R	K	E	T
T	X	B	O	Z	F	K	J	E	K	W
A	I	Q	E	A	G	E	R	S	H	G
L	Z	T	D	B	C	R	W	F	X	D
L	F	Y	N	V	J	S	C	G	M	K

2 ☆ **Write the correct name under each picture.**

bookshop chemist's cinema ~~clothes shop~~ games shop hairdresser's newsagent's phone shop shoe shop sports shop stationery shop

1 *clothes shop*

2 ______

3 ______

4 ______

5 ______

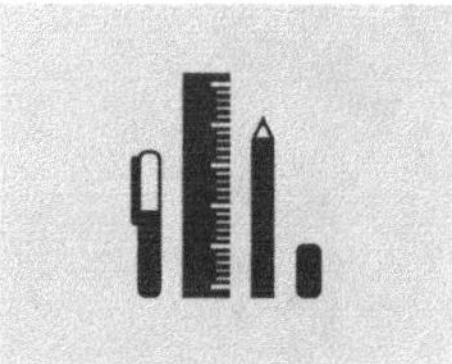

6 ______

7 ______

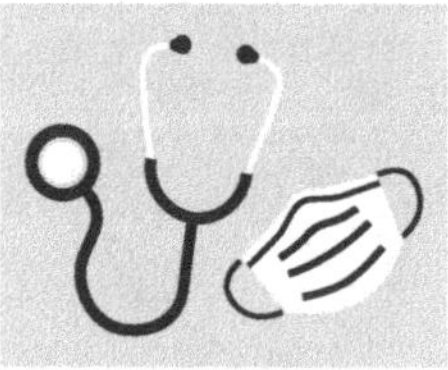

8 ______

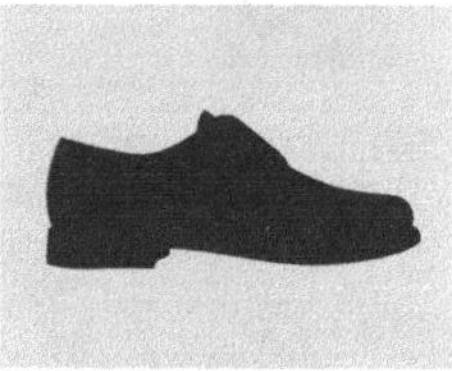

9 ______

10 ______

11 ______

3 ☆☆ **Tick (✔) the correct sentences.**

1 You go to a shoe shop to buy bread. ☐
2 You go to a bookshop to buy paper, notebooks and pens. ☐
3 You go to a restaurant to buy drinks and snacks, like soup or a sandwich. ☐
4 You go to a cinema to watch a film. ☐
5 You go to a sports shop to buy computer games. ☐
6 You go to a hairdresser's to buy all types of food and things for the home. ☐

4 ☆☆ **Correct the sentences in exercise 3.**

1 *You go to a baker's to buy bread.*
2 ______
3 ______
4 ______
5 ______
6 ______

5 ☆☆☆ **Which places do you visit in a shopping centre when … ?**

1 you're hungry
______
2 you have birthday money to spend
______
3 it's Saturday and you're with your friends
______

there is/are

1 ☆ **Choose the correct option.**

1 There **is/are** a supermarket in the shopping centre.
2 There **is/are** three cafés.
3 There **isn't/aren't** any bookshops.
4 There **isn't/are** a games shop.
5 There **is/are** some food stalls.
6 There **is/are** a lot of clothes shops.

2 ☆☆ **Write all the possible sentences you can make with a word from each cloud.**

There

a
any
some
a lot of

's
isn't
are
aren't

cinema.
restaurants.

____
____
____
____

3 ☆☆ **Match questions 1–5 with answers a–e.**

1 Are there lots of shops on the ship? *d*
2 What about food? Are there any places to eat? ___
3 And what about entertainment? ___
4 I haven't got anything to read. Is there a bookshop? ___
5 Is there a supermarket? ___

a There are lots! From big restaurants to cafés for your morning coffee.
b Yes, there is. A cruise is the perfect place to do some summer reading.
c No, there isn't! You're on holiday – you can forget about shopping for food.
d Yes, there are. We've got everything from technology to clothes.
e There's a fantastic cinema with new films every day.

4 ☆☆ **Write complete questions and answers about a school.**

1 a shop? / No
Is there a shop?
No, there isn't.
2 an art room? / Yes
____
____
3 rooms for practising music? / Yes
____
____
4 Wi-Fi in the school? / No
____
____
5 computers in the classrooms? / No
____
____
6 students from other countries? / Yes
____
____
7 a cafeteria? / Yes
____
____

5 ☆☆☆ **Answer the questions in exercise 4 about your school. You can include extra information.**

1 ______________________________
2 ______________________________
3 ______________________________
4 ______________________________
5 ______________________________
6 ______________________________
7 ______________________________

An online recommendation

Eating Out CALIFORNIA: ______

In most restaurants, you order your food, someone cooks it for you in the restaurant's kitchen and a waiter brings the food to your table. But now there's a new type of restaurant where *you* are the cook: make-it-yourself restaurants.

If you like Asian food, why not try the Little Sheep Mongolian Hot Pot restaurant in San Francisco? There are all types of vegetables, fish and meat on the table and you cook the food in hot soup in the centre.

I love bread and cheese, so it's no surprise that I also love fondue. My favourite restaurant is the Melting Pot in Sacramento, but there are three more Melting Pots in California. And if you're not in California, there are another 94 restaurants in the United States, Mexico and Canada. It's not a problem if you don't like cheese: you can also eat a great chocolate fondue!

Why pay to eat in a restaurant and then cook the food yourself? Because it's the perfect way to have a good time with your friends and family.

A

B

Subskill: Understanding the general idea

Just try to get a general idea the first time you read. Don't stop if there's a word you don't know.

1 ☆ 12 **Read and listen to the text and complete the title of the article with the best option.**

- **a** my favourite restaurants
- **b** a new type of restaurant
- **c** California's best restaurants

2 ☆☆ **Look at photos A and B. What dishes can you see?**

A ______

B ______

3 ☆☆ **Complete the table with information about the two restaurants in the text.**

Name	Where is it?	What's in the pot?
1	2	*Hot soup, meat, fish and vegetables*
3	4	5

4 ☆☆☆ **Match 1–5 with a–e to make sentences.**

1 In most restaurants *c*
2 In this new type of restaurant, ___
3 The Little Sheep restaurant is good for ___
4 There are Melting Pot restaurants ___
5 A make-it-yourself restaurant is a nice ___

- **a** people who like Asian food.
- **b** in the USA, Mexico and Canada.
- **c** another person cooks the food.
- **d** place to spend an evening with friends.
- **e** you cook the food.

5 ☆☆☆ **What type of restaurant do you like? Why?**

______
______
______
______

A conversation

1 ☆ Look at the photo and complete the sentences with your ideas.

1 The chefs are …
   a at home.
   b in a restaurant.
   c at school.
2 It is …
   a a class.
   b a competition.
   c a celebration.

2 ☆☆ 🔊13 Listen to a conversation and check your answers in exercise 1.

▶ Subskill: Taking notes while you listen

Don't write complete sentences when you listen. Write short notes about the things you hear.

3 ☆☆☆ Listen and complete the notes.

1 The competition is at Jesse's *school* .
2 The students are in teams of ______ .
3 They have just ______ minutes to cook.
4 It has to be a healthy meal with meat or tofu, vegetables and ______ .
5 You can only spend ______ on each meal.
6 Jesse and his team are making ______ .

Ordering food

1 ☆ Match 1–6 with a–f to make phrases for ordering food.

1 Can I — b
2 I'd like
3 Would you like
4 Have you got any
5 Would you like anything
6 How much

a to drink?
b have (a burger), please?
c fruit?
d some juice.
e is that?
f any (fries) with that?

2 ☆☆ Who says each phrase? Write C (customer) or W (waiter).

1 ___ 4 ___
2 ___ 5 ___
3 ___ 6 ___

3 ☆☆☆ Complete the conversations.

Conversation 1

Would you 1 *like anything* to drink?

I'd 2 ______ some juice.

What type?

Have you 3 ______ ______ orange juice?

Yes, here you are.

Conversation 2

Can 4 ______ ______ some tomato soup, please?

Of course. 5 ______ ______ ______ any bread with that?

Yes please. How 6 ______ ______ ______ ?

Three pounds fifty.

A blog post about food

1 ☆ **Complete the sentences with *and* or *but*.**

1 The restaurant is expensive *but* the food is delicious!
2 I'd like some pasta ____________ some water.
3 There are some cafés ____________ there aren't any food stalls.
4 I've got three aunts ____________ I haven't got any uncles.
5 The city is noisy ____________ the country is quiet.
6 There's a pencil case ____________ two notebooks in my bag.

2 ☆☆ **Read the phrases. Do they describe a dish (D), give an opinion about it (O) or say how to make it (H)?**

1 It's a type of cake. *D*
2 I love it! ___
3 You make it with cheese and tomatoes. ___
4 It's delicious. ___
5 You cook meat with vegetables. ___
6 It's a fish dish with potatoes. ___

3 ☆☆☆ **Write a blog post about your favourite dish.**

Super skills

COLLABORATION SUPER SKILLS

It's important to work well together.

Choose which answer is better to respond to sentences 1–3.

1 What do you think about organising a cooking competition?
   a No. I want to organise a football match.
   (b) That's a good idea, but let's think about other options.
2 I can write the text, find the photos and make the posters.
   a Why don't we share the work?
   b OK.
3 How can we organise the party?
   a I can buy food and you buy the drinks.
   b You can do the shopping.

Vocabulary review

Food and drink

1 Complete the mind map with words in the box.

apple	banana	biscuit	chocolate
coffee	juice	orange	pea
potato	tea	~~tomato~~	water

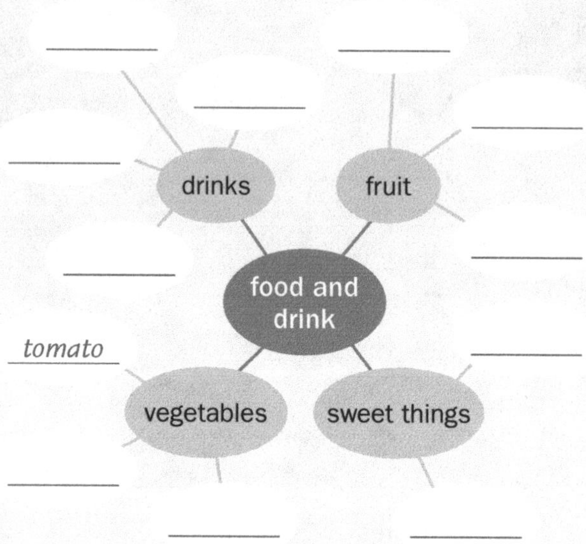

The shopping centre

2 Write where you can buy each of the things on the shopping list. Don't write *supermarket*.

1 bread *baker's*
2 a computer game ____________
3 a mobile phone ____________
4 a sandwich ____________
5 a pencil case ____________

3 Write where the people are.

1 'Have you got *The Hobbit* by J.R.R Tolkien?' *bookshop*
2 'I'd like the fish, please.' ____________
3 'Have you got these jeans in black?' ____________
4 'Two tickets for *Space Adventure* at 4:30 pm, please.' ____________
5 'Have you got any golf balls?' ____________
6 'I'd like these trainers, but in a 39, please.' ____________

Grammar review

Countable and uncountable nouns

1 Complete the sentences with *a, an* or *some*.

1 For my snack today, I've got ___*an*___ apple.
2 We've got ________ tomatoes.
3 I'd like ________ bread, please.
4 Can I have ________ cheese sandwich?
5 To make this juice, use ________ orange and two bananas.

some, any, a lot of

2 Complete the message with *some, any* or *a lot of*.

I can cook dinner, but there are 1 ___*some*___ other things to do. Can you go to the supermarket? Don't buy 2 ________ pasta (we've got 3 ________ spaghetti – six or seven packets!), but please get 4 ________ tomatoes. We haven't got 5 ________ cheese – please buy 6 ________. And we haven't got 7 ________ drinks, so please buy some juice.

there is/are

3 Complete the sentences with the correct form of *there is/are*.

Frieda: 1 ___*Are there*___ any cinemas near your house?
Julen: Yes, 2 ________. 3 ________ a big cinema about ten minutes from home.
Frieda: 4 ________ a lot of screens?
Julen: Yes, 5 ________. 6 ________ ten different films at the same time.
Frieda: Is there only one cinema near your house?
Julen: No, 7 ________. 8 ________ also a small one. It's only got one screen.

Round-up 1 2 3 4 5 6 7 8

Choose the correct option.

Rotterdam's Fenix Food Factory

1 Have you got/You have got a free day in Rotterdam? The Fenix Food Factory is **2 an/a** great place to visit and **3 are/there are** a lot of things to do. The market **4 is/it's** open Tuesday to Saturday. It's a good place for shopping and **5 it's/its** food stalls have got **6 a lot of/lot of** different things to buy. They've got **7 some/any** fantastic fruit, vegetables and cheese, and the bread is delicious!

8 Is there/Are there other things to do? Yes, **9 they're/there are**. **10 They got/They've got** jazz concerts each week and they **11 has/have** got a games evening on Tuesdays. And for €10, **12 there are/there's** a market tour – it finishes with a snack and a drink.

Self-evaluation

Read the objectives for this unit. How well can you now do each one? Put a tick (✔).

	😀	😐	🙁
1 I can talk about food and drink.	☐	☐	☐
2 I can talk about places in a shopping centre.	☐	☐	☐
3 I can use *a, an, some, any* and *a lot of*.	☐	☐	☐
4 I can describe things with *there is/are*.	☐	☐	☐
5 I can understand the general idea of a text.	☐	☐	☐
6 I can take notes when I listen.	☐	☐	☐
7 I can order food.	☐	☐	☐
8 I can write a blog post.	☐	☐	☐

If you choose 🙁, ask your teacher for some extra help.

Grammar reference and practice pp88–89

4 My time

Vocabulary

The time; daily routines

1 ☆ **Tick the clocks with the right time. Correct the times which are incorrect.**

① 

half past eight

✗ *It's half past six.*

② 

half past two

③ 

ten o'clock

④ 

quarter past eleven

⑤ 

twenty-five past four

⑥ 

twenty to five

2 ☆☆ **Write another way to say the time.**

1 It's 6:30. *It's half past six.*
2 It's a quarter past seven.
______
3 It's 4:50. ______
4 It's twenty-five to two.
______
5 It's 12:15. ______
6 It's midday. ______

3 ☆☆ **Match verbs in box A with words in box B to describe activities in a daily routine. Which verb doesn't match with a word in B?**

A

~~do~~ finish get go have relax start

B

~~homework~~ lunch school school to bed up

do homework
______
______

4 ☆☆☆ **Complete the text with activities and times from the table. Add verbs and write the times in full.**

get up	7:15
breakfast	7:25
go to school	8:00
have lessons	8:55–3:15
lunch	12:30
homework	4:00–6:45
have dinner	6:50
bed	9:30

I get up at **1** *quarter past seven* and I **2** ______ at about twenty-five past seven. I go to school at **3** ______. We have lessons from five to nine to **4** ______, and we have a break for lunch at half past twelve. I get home at four o'clock and then I **5** ______. I finish it at about a quarter to seven. After dinner, I relax for a couple of hours and I **6** ______ at about half past nine.

5 ☆☆☆ **Write a description of your daily routine.**

______
______
______
______
______

Present simple: affirmative

1 ☆ Complete the table with the *he/she/it* form of the verbs in the box.

be do finish ~~get~~ go have make relax start study teach try want

+ *s*	+ *es*	change *y* to *ies*	irregular
gets			

2 ☆☆ Write complete sentences with the correct form of the verb.

1 From Monday to Friday / Thea / get up / eight o'clock
From Monday to Friday, Thea gets up at eight o'clock.

2 James / finish school / two o'clock / Fridays
____

3 We / go to bed / 10:30 / at weekends
____

4 Mrs Phipps / teach / English and history
____

5 I / relax / when / finish my homework
____

6 Clara / do her homework / when / get home from school
____

Present simple: negative

3 ☆☆ Complete the sentences with *don't* or *doesn't*.

1 School children in Japan *don't* have long holidays. They study for 230 days a year.

2 My Korean friend, Min-Seo, __________ have free time on Saturday mornings: she has school!

3 In Russia, students study with the same people from 6 to 16 years old. They __________ change school.

4 My cousin Torsten lives in Germany. He __________ go to school. He starts next year.

5 Students in Kenya __________ wear their own clothes. They wear a uniform.

6 Classes in Australia __________ have a lot of students. A typical class has got 18 students.

4 ☆☆ Complete the sentences with the correct form of the verb.

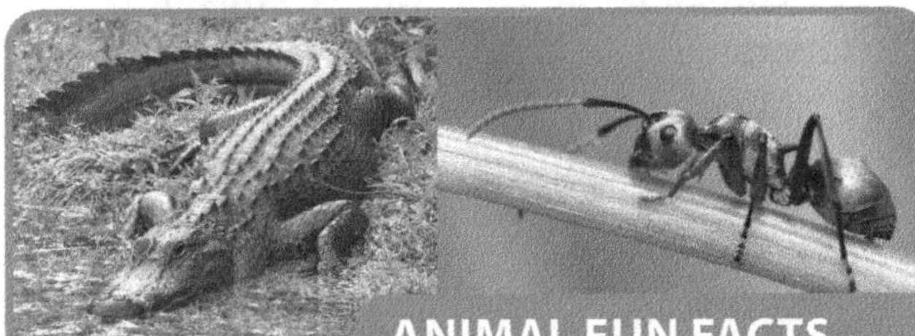

ANIMAL FUN FACTS

1 An American alligator *lives* **(live +)** for 30 to 50 years.

2 An ant __________ **(sleep –)**.

3 Dolphins __________ **(see +)** in black and white.

4 A cow __________ **(stand +)** facing north or south, never east or west.

5 Some tarantulas __________ **(eat –)** for two years.

6 An elephant __________ **(drink +)** 200 litres of water a day.

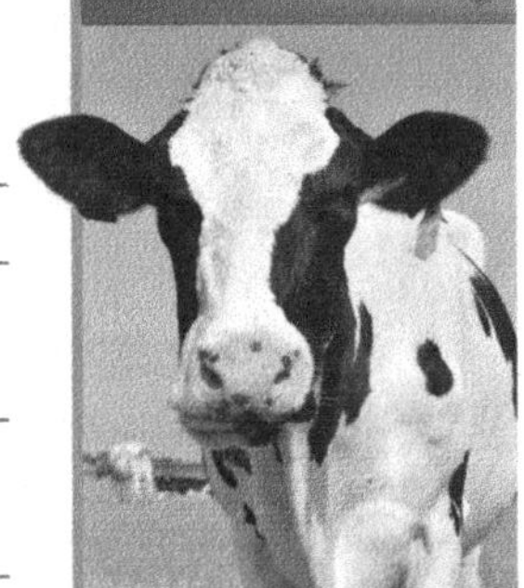

5 ☆☆☆ Complete the text with the correct form of the verbs.

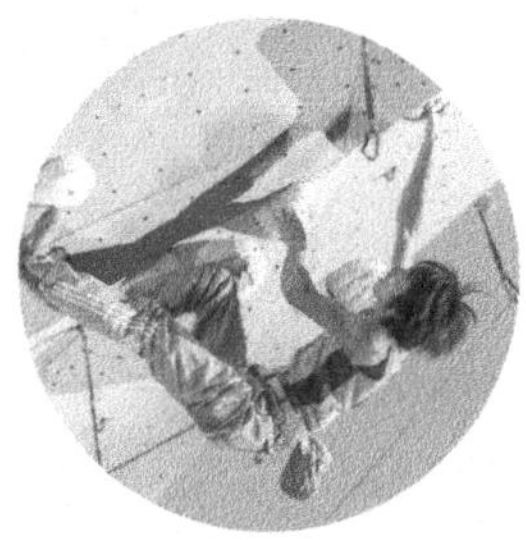

Sachi Amma is a World Champion climber from Japan. What's a typical morning for Sachi when he's at home? Sachi **1** *gets up* **(get up)** at about 7:00 am. He **2** __________ **(not train)** in the morning, but after he gets up, he **3** __________ **(do)** yoga at home. After that he **4** __________ **(make)** a big glass of juice for breakfast. Later, he **5** __________ **(go)** to a café and does some work on his computer. He **6** __________ **(have)** lunch in a restaurant where they **7** __________ **(make)** fantastic udon noodles. This is important: noodles **8** __________ **(give)** Sachi energy for climbing. In the afternoon, he **9** __________ **(go)** to the gym to do his training, and that's when the real work **10** __________ **(start)**.

Grammar reference and practice pp90–91

Free-time activities

1 ☆ **Complete the verbs with the missing letters.**

1 d *o*
2 ch __ t
3 t __ k __
4 m __ __ t
5 w __ t __ h
6 __ iste __

2 ☆ **Match the verbs in exercise 1 with a word or phrase in the box to describe the free-time activities in the photos.**

friends   on my phone
photos   sport   to music   ~~TV~~

1 *watch TV*

2 ______

3 ______

4 ______

5 ______

6 ______

3 ☆☆ **Complete the table with the words in the box.**

basketball   out on my bike   shopping
swimming   the guitar   the piano
~~to the cinema~~   video games

go	play
to the cinema	

4 ☆☆ **Choose the correct option.**

1 I **go shopping/do sport** at the shopping centre.
2 Lola **goes swimming/plays video games** in her room.
3 We **do sport/go out on our bikes** at school.
4 I **meet my friends/play the piano** in the park.
5 My friends **listen to music/watch TV** at parties.
6 Freddy **plays the guitar/reads** in the English class.

5 ☆☆ **Complete the sentences with the correct form of the verbs in the box.**

do sport   go swimming   read
~~sleep~~   take photos   watch TV

1 I normally *sleep* for eight hours every night.
2 Ben ______ two days a week. On Mondays he plays tennis and on Fridays he does judo.
3 I ______ three or four pages of my book before I go to sleep.
4 Felix has got a good camera and he ______ with his uncle.
5 Mum ______ every evening, but it's very boring. I prefer series online.
6 When we're on holiday at the beach, we ______ all the time, some days in the sea and other days in the pool.

6 ☆☆ **Complete the sentences about free-time activities for you.**

1 After school, I ______.
2 In the holidays, I ______.
3 When I'm with my friends, we ______ ______.

Present simple: *Yes/No* questions and short answers

1 ☆ **Complete the questions with *do* or *does*.**

1 ___*Do*___ penguins live in the Arctic?
2 ______ February have 30 days?
3 ______ some French children go to school on Saturdays?
4 ______ Brazilian people speak Spanish?
5 ______ a guitarist play a musical instrument?
6 ______ a jellyfish sleep?

2 ☆☆ **Match the questions in exercise 1 with the short answers in the box.**

Yes, he/she does.	Yes, they do.	No, it doesn't.
No, it doesn't.	~~No, they don't.~~	No, they don't.

1 *No, they don't.*
2 ______
3 ______
4 ______
5 ______
6 ______

Present simple: *Wh-* questions

3 ☆ **Complete the table with the question words in the box.**

what	when	where	~~who~~

1 *who*	2 ______	3 ______	4 ______

4 ☆☆☆ **Complete the questions.**

1 ___*When*___ do you go to bed?
2 ______ do you do on Saturday mornings?
3 Where ______ your best friend live?
4 ______ do your parents get home from work?
5 Who ______ you go to school with?
6 ______ languages does your mother speak?

love/like/don't like/hate + noun

5 ☆☆ **Read the sentences and disagree with the statements using *love/hate*.**

1 Thelma doesn't like basketball.
Yes, she does. She loves it.
2 Alex and Gemma don't like *Spider-Man* films.
______
3 Bruno hates K-pop.
______
4 We don't like Dylan Minnette.
______
5 Bea loves bananas.
______
6 I don't like Taylor Swift.
______

6 ☆☆☆ **Order the words to make questions, then answer them.**

1 go / you / Where / on holiday / do ?
Where do you go on holiday?
______
2 in your free time / you / What / do / do ?
______
______
3 have / Who / do / breakfast with / you ?
______
______
4 at weekends / When / get up / you / do ?
______
______

Grammar reference and practice pp90–91

An online article

TOP 5 FACTS ABOUT ... TIME ZONES

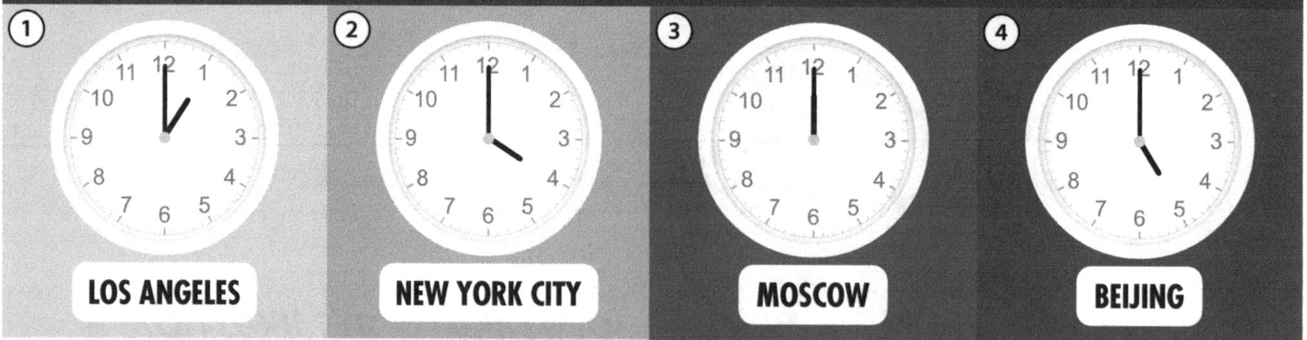

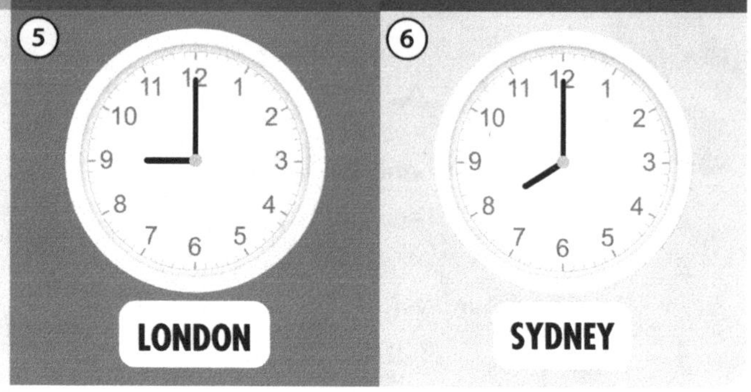

1 There are 24 hours in a day, so is the world divided into 24 time zones? No, it isn't. There are 38 time zones! All countries use Greenwich Mean Time (GMT) from Greenwich, London as the starting point. Countries are either ahead of or behind GMT.

2 There are 11 time zones in Russia. Pavel has breakfast in Moscow at 7:00 am. But for his cousin Katya in Vladivostok it's 2:00 pm. It takes eight hours to fly from Vladivostok to Moscow, but if Katya flies at 7:00 pm she gets to Moscow at 8:00 pm the same day!

3 With 9,597 million square kilometres, China is a very big country. So it's got a lot of time zones, right? No, it hasn't. China has got only one enormous time zone.

4 The International Space Station moves all the time, so which time zone is it in? That's easy. The ISS has the same time as Greenwich.

5 Do you want to celebrate your birthday twice? No problem. Start in Samoa and go just 50 kilometres (25 minutes by plane) to American Samoa. When you travel, you cross the International Date Line and your birthday starts all over again!

1 ☆ **Look at the clocks and write the time.**

1 *It's one o'clock in Los Angeles.*
2 ______
3 ______
4 ______
5 ______
6 ______

2 ☆☆ 14 **Read and listen to the text and match paragraphs 1–5 with headings a–e.**

a A big country with a lot of time zones ___
b All time starts in London *1*
c A 48-hour party ___
d What's the time in space? ___
e A big country with only one time zone ___

Subskill: Reading for detail

To find details, read the questions first. Then look for the information in the text.

3 ☆☆☆ **Read the text and choose the correct answer.**

1 How many time zones are there?
a 24 **b** 12 (**c**) 38

2 Where is Greenwich?
a Paris **b** London **c** New York

3 How many hours' difference are there between Moscow and Vladivostok?
a 7 **b** 11 **c** 8

4 How long does it take to fly from Vladivostok to Moscow?
a 7 hours **b** 1 hour **c** 8 hours

5 How long does it take to go from Samoa to American Samoa by plane?
a 25 minutes **b** 48 hours **c** 50 minutes

4 ☆☆☆ **Answer the questions for you.**

1 How many time zones are there in your country?
______

2 Is the time in your country the same or different to GMT?
______

3 Does the time change in winter and summer where you live?
______

A welcome meeting

1 ☆ 🔊15 **Look at the two photos. Listen to the first part of the audio. Which situation is it, A or B?**

A

B

2 ☆☆ **Listen to the complete talk. Choose the correct sentences.**

1 The speaker is the director of the school. ☑
2 The students are on an English language course in the UK. ☐
3 The students have classes all day. ☐
4 The students go to famous cities during their visit. ☐

Subskill: Listening to complete sentences

Listen carefully for the words you see in the first part of the sentence.

3 ☆☆☆ **Listen again and complete the sentences.**

1 Angela Cox is the director of *the school* .
2 From Monday to Friday students get up at ______ .
3 On Mondays, Tuesdays, Thursdays and Fridays, there are lessons ______ .
4 Lunch is at ______ .
5 In 'Use your English' students do projects like making ______ .
6 In the afternoon, students can do sports or ______ .
7 One day they have a quiz, another evening there is ______ .
8 On Wednesdays, there are ______ .
9 On Saturday this week, there is a visit to ______ .

Making plans

1 ☆☆ **Complete the phrases with the words in the box.**

about busy fine free ~~go~~ good OK yes

1 Why don't we *go* to the cinema?
2 Are you ______ on Tuesday?
3 OK, ______ .
4 What ______ Saturday afternoon?
5 Sorry, I'm ______ .
6 Is Friday ______ ?
7 ______ , great.
8 Thursday's ______ .

2 ☆ **Write M (making suggestions) or A (answering) for the phrases in exercise 1.**

1 *M*
2 ___
3 ___
4 ___
5 ___
6 ___
7 ___
8 ___

3 ☆☆☆ **Complete the dialogue with the missing questions in the box.**

Are you free on Friday? ~~Do you want to meet this weekend?~~ Is three o'clock OK? OK fine. What time? What about Saturday?

1 *Do you want to meet this weekend?*

Yes, great.

2 ______

No, sorry, I'm busy on Friday.

3 ______

Saturday's good. Why don't we go to the park and play basketball?

4 ______

5 ______

Yes, perfect. See you at 3:00 pm.

Notes and messages

1 ☆ **Complete the sentences with *because* and the information in brackets.**

1 The shopping centre is a good place to eat **(there are lots of cafés)**
because there are lots of cafés .

2 I'm not free this afternoon **(I've got an exam)**
______________ .

3 Ben doesn't eat meat and fish **(he's a vegetarian)**
______________ .

4 I speak Spanish **(my mum's from Spain)**
______________ .

2 ☆☆ **Match messages 1–2 with answers A–B.**

1 Hi Brandon!
Do you want to meet this evening and study together for the maths exam?

2 I'm not home for dinner tonight because I've got a meeting. There's some rice and vegetables on the table.

A OK that's fine, Dad. See you later.

B Sorry, I'm busy this evening because it's my dad's birthday. What about tomorrow?

3 ☆☆☆ **Write two messages. For each one, choose a person in box A and a situation in box B. Include *because* in your messages.**

A	B
a friend your mother or father	try to meet ask for help

Super skills

COMMUNICATION

SUPER SKILLS

When you work together, it's important to ask for and give help.

1 Choose the best answer to ask for help.
a Tell me what to do.
b What do you think of this?

2 Which is a good way to answer?
a That's really bad!
b I like this part, but what about using more colour?

Vocabulary review

The time

1 Order the times in the box from 12:00 to 5:00.

2:55 3:45 4:35 ~~12:05~~
quarter past three quarter to five
half past four half past twelve
one o'clock twenty past two

12:05 ______________

____

Daily routines

2 Complete the sentences with the correct form of the verbs in the box.

do homework ~~get up~~ have breakfast
have dinner have lessons have lunch

1 Jake *gets up* at 7:00 am on Mondays.
2 I don't normally ______________ with my mum because she goes to work before I get up.
3 Clara ______________ at home, but some of her friends eat at school.
4 We ______________ from 9:00 am to 3:30 pm.
5 Freya doesn't ______________ on Saturdays. She does it all on Sundays.
6 We ______________ when my dad gets home at about 7:00 pm.

Free-time activities

3 Complete the text about Jonah's free-time activities.

I don't **1** *do* sport apart from PE lessons at school. Other people in my class **2** ______________ basketball all the time. They also **3** ______________ video games, but I prefer to do other things. I **4** ______________ photos. I also really like music. I **5** ______________ the piano and the trumpet and I **6** ______________ to music all the time. I also **7** ______________ books about music. At weekends, I **8** ______________ friends and we **9** ______________ to the cinema. The most important thing about the film for me is the music!

Grammar review

Present simple: affirmative and negative

1 Change *I* sentences to *Tania* and *Tania* sentences to *I*.

1 I have breakfast and then I go to school.
Tania has breakfast and then she goes to school.

2 Tania loves sport and on Fridays she plays basketball.

______

3 I relax when I get home from school.

______

4 I don't have lunch at school.

______

5 After school, Tania meets her friends and they go shopping.

______

Present simple: questions

2 Order the words to make *Wh-* and *Yes/No* questions.

1 do / What time / get up / you ?
What time do you get up?

2 like / video games / Do / you ?

______

3 brother / does / Where / to school / your / go ?

______

4 work / in a hospital / your parents / Do ?

______

5 go to bed / When / you / do / at the weekend ?

______

love/like/don't like/hate + object pronoun

3 Answer the questions with *love* (♥♥), *like* (♥), *don't like* (☹) or *hate* (☹☹) and an object pronoun.

1 Do you like cats? I ♥♥
Yes, I do. I love them.

2 Does Karina like rap music? She ♥♥

______

3 Does Nacho like Millie Bobby Brown? He ☹

______

4 Do you like coffee and tea? I ☹☹

______

5 Does your mother like cooking? She ☹☹

______

Round-up 1 2 3 4 5 6 7 8

Choose the correct option.

A normal teenager?

Coco Gauff **1 are/is** a 16-year-old girl from the USA. She lives in Florida with **2 she/her** mum and dad and she **3 got/'s got** two brothers. Her **4 brother's/brothers'** names are Cody and Cameron.

5 Coco is/Is Coco different from other teenagers?

Yes, **6 she is/she's**. Coco is an amazing tennis player. She **7 play/plays** in tournaments such as Wimbledon and the US Open. She **8 doesn't go/don't go** to school. Her mum **9 teach/teaches** her at home because she spends **10 a lot of/any** time on the tennis court.

11 Does she do/Does she any free-time activities?

Yes, **12 she does/she has**. She **13 listen/listens** to music and **14 does go/goes** to concerts. She also likes TikTok and basketball.

Self-evaluation

Read the objectives for this unit. How well can you now do each one? Put a tick (✔).

	😀	😐	☹
1 I can tell the time.	☐	☐	☐
2 I can talk about daily routine and free-time activities.	☐	☐	☐
3 I can use the present simple to talk about regular activities.	☐	☐	☐
4 I can talk about likes and dislikes.	☐	☐	☐
5 I can read to find detailed information.	☐	☐	☐
6 I can listen to complete information.	☐	☐	☐
7 I can make suggestions.	☐	☐	☐
8 I can write messages.	☐	☐	☐

If you choose ☹, ask your teacher for some extra help.

5 Tech life

Vocabulary

Abilities

1 ☆ **Write the abilities.**

1 c *o* *o* *k*

2 r __ __

3 p __ __ __

4 s __ __ __

5 w __ __ __

6 d __ __ __ __

2 ☆☆ **Match the verbs in box A with the words in box B to make expressions.**

A

call catch
~~fly~~ play (x2)
send talk

B

a ball a friend
~~a plane~~
a text message
tennis the guitar
with your friend

fly a plane
____
____
____
____
____
____

3 ☆☆ **Complete the table with the activities in the box. You can use some activities more than once.**

~~add numbers~~ carry a bag clean your room climb a mountain jump into a swimming pool repair your bike speak another language spell a word tell stories to your little brother wash your face

at school	*add numbers*
on holiday	
at home	

4 ☆☆☆ **Complete the sentences with the correct expression in exercises 2 and 3.**

1 When you play basketball, you *catch a ball* .
2 When you do a maths exam, you ____________ .
3 If you don't want to speak on the phone, you ____________ .
4 When you go shopping, you ____________ .
5 If you don't know how to write something, ask the teacher to ____________ .

5 ☆☆☆ **Complete the questions. Then answer them for you.**

1 Do you know how to *repair* your bike?
____
2 On a typical day, how many times do you ________ a text message?
____
3 Would you like to ________ another language? Which language?
____
4 Can you ________ a musical instrument?
____
5 Do you prefer to ________ into a swimming pool or get into the water slowly?
____

can and *can't*

1 ☆ Write complete sentences with *can*.

1 Callum / dance **(–)**
Callum can't dance.

2 Katriona / speak French **(+)**
______

3 I / cook **(–)**
______

4 My aunt / fly a plane **(+)**
______

5 My friends and I / play golf **(+)**
______

6 Lewis / sing **(–)**
______

2 ☆☆ Write complete questions with *can* and the verbs in the box.

cook dance ~~repair~~ run speak talk

1 you / your bike ?
Can you repair your bike?

2 you / pizza ?
______

3 your best friend / another language ?
______

4 your parents / the tango ?
______

5 you / 100 metres in 10 seconds ?
______

6 you / with your friend and do your homework at the same time ?
______

3 ☆☆ Match the questions in exercise 2 with answers a–f.

a Yes, they can. My dad's quite good, but my mum's not a great dancer! ___
b Yes, I can. But it helps if another person can hold it. *1*
c No, I can't. I'm not Usain Bolt! ___
d I think I can, but my mum doesn't! ___
e No, I can't. But I can make spaghetti. ___
f No, she can't, but her mum can speak Japanese. ___

4 ☆☆ Choose the correct question.

1 (a) Who can I ask for help?
  b Who I can ask for help?
2 a Where can we catch the bus?
  b Where we can catch the bus?
3 a Which can you speak languages?
  b Which languages can you speak?
4 a What instrument you can play?
  b What instrument can you play?
5 a When can you get here?
  b When can get you here?

5 ☆☆☆ Choose the correct option.

THE AMAZING OSTRICH

1 (Can all birds fly?)/All birds can fly? No, **2 they can't/they don't can**. The ostrich is an unusual bird. First, it's very big. Ostriches **3 can to be/can be** 2.7 m tall and weigh 145 kilos. They **4 can run/can runs** very fast: some ostriches can run 70 kilometres per hour. The ostrich can also jump and swim! But there's one thing the ostrich **5 can't do/don't can do**: it **6 can't to fly/can't fly**.

Technology nouns; adjectives

1 ☆ **Look at the photos and complete the crossword.**

1

2

3
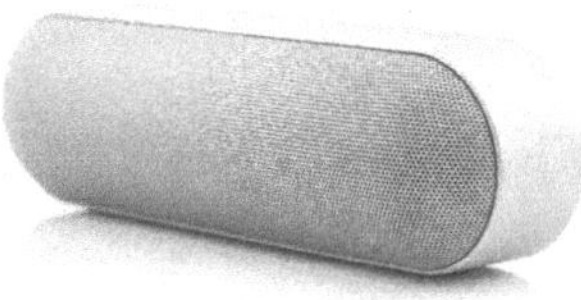

4

5

6

7

8
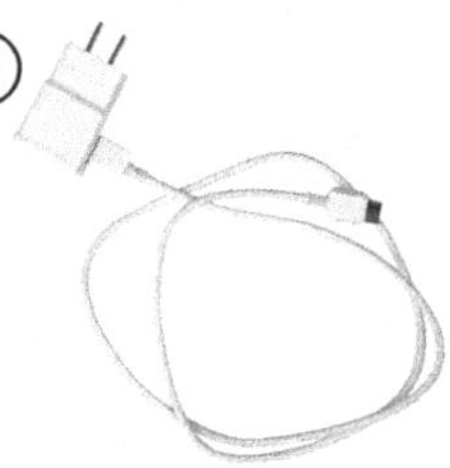

2 ☆☆ **The words in bold are in the wrong sentence. Correct the sentences.**

1 Can I use your **screen**? My phone battery is on 10%. charger
2 My phone has got an excellent **touchpad**. It takes really good photos. ______
3 My grandmother doesn't like using a **camera**. She prefers a mouse. ______
4 I use a big computer for my homework, but I prefer a **keyboard** to use on the train. ______
5 The computer **charger** is very small. I can't see very well from here. ______
6 Oh, that's an interesting **tablet**: are those Arabic letters? ______

3 ☆ **Complete the adjectives with the missing letters.**

1 ch e a p
2 d _ f _ _ c _ _ _
3 e _ _ y
4 _ _ p _ n _ _ ve
5 f _ _ t
6 _ _ avy
7 _ _ ght
8 _ l _ w

4 ☆☆ **Choose the correct option.**

Archie: Is that your **1 new/easy** phone?
Lou: Yes – here you are.
Archie: Wow – it's very **2 light/slow**.
Lou: Yes, it's only 113 grams. It's very **3 difficult/fast** too. My old phone is very slow now.
Archie: It's a different brand from your old phone – is it **4 difficult/cheap** to use?
Lou: No, it's very easy.
Archie: And what about the price? Is the new one very **5 fast/expensive**?
Lou: Yes, that's why it's my birthday present from Mum, Dad and Grandma.

5 ☆☆☆ **What technology do you use and why? Write your answers.**

1 For homework
______
2 For taking photos
______
3 For talking with your friends
______
4 For listening to music
______

Comparative adjectives

1 ☆ Complete the table with the missing words.

Adjective	Comparative adjective
1 *clean*	cleaner
young	2
hot	3
4	worse
ugly	5
dangerous	6
7	better
thin	8
interesting	9

2 ☆☆ Complete the advertisements with the comparative form of the adjective.

The EasyPic 101:
1 *Smaller* **(small)**,
2 ______ **(light)**
and **3** ______ **(easy)**
than your old camera and it takes **4** ______ **(good)**
pictures.

Come and try the new Megaplex cinema:
5 ______ **(big)** and **6** ______
(modern) than the old cinema and this week it's **7** ______ **(cheap)** too with our 50% off special opening offer.

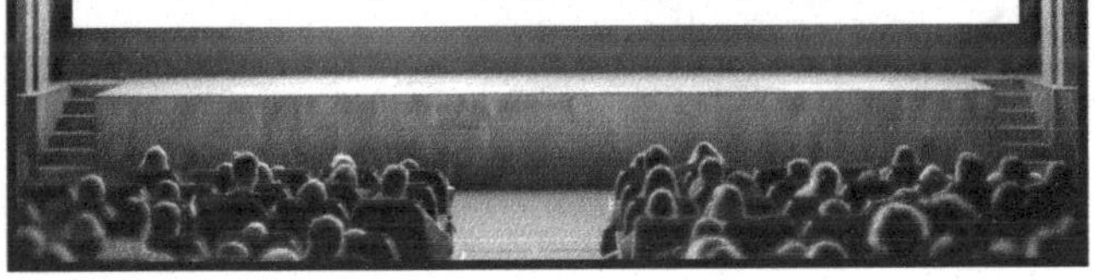

3 ☆☆☆ Write a new sentence with the opposite adjective so it means the same as the first.

1 London is bigger than Manchester.
Manchester is smaller than London.

2 The country is quieter than the city.
______

3 The small shops are emptier than the supermarket.
______

4 Maths is more difficult than English.
______

5 My mum's hair is curlier than my hair.
______

6 The food stall is cheaper than the café.
______

Possessive pronouns

4 ☆☆ Rewrite the sentences with possessive pronouns.

1 Those are Jim's pens.
Those are his.

2 It's my bag.
______

3 That's our bus.
______

4 It's Carl and Erica's dog.
______

5 It's Maria's camera.
______

6 **A:** Is this my book? **B:** Yes, it's your book.
______

5 ☆☆☆ Complete the conversations with possessive pronouns.

1 **Lea:** Excuse me, is this chair free?
Woman: No, it's *mine*. You can have that one.

2 **Mar:** Have we got a table?
Lea: Yes, the table next to the window – that's ______.

3 **Mar:** Excuse me, is this bag ______?
Man: No, it's ______, but I can move it. She's my sister.

4 **Waiter:** Number 26. Cheese and tomato pizza.
Lea: Ooh – that's ______. Here, please!

5 **Lea:** Which is my drink?
Mar: Let's see – this one is ______.

5 Reading

A magazine article

VOICE RECOGNITION TECHNOLOGY:

a normal part of 21st-century life

A cheap way to have a smart home

More and more people have voice recognition machines in their homes. You give an instruction and the machine can turn on the lights or control the TV. And they're cheaper than a lot of technology. Amazon's Echo Dot plays music and answers questions, and it only costs $30.

'Siri – do my homework!'

How do you check words and information? Do you use a dictionary or a book? If you're a teenager, then your answer is probably 'Ask Siri'; a recent study shows that 55% of teens use a virtual assistant like Apple's Siri, Microsoft's Cortana or Amazon's Alexa every day. And they're very popular with younger children, too.

Are young people less polite because of voice recognition?

Some people worry that young people's language is ruder because of these machines. Older adults use expressions like 'Please, Alexa' and 'Thank you, Siri', but experts say it's more normal to just give an instruction: 'Cortana, tell me ...' 'Siri, what's ... ?'. They think that children hear this and think it's OK to talk to people the same way.

Part of our lives

Some people like voice recognition machines. Other people don't like the idea. But love them or hate them, most people think that voice recognition machines are part of our lives now.

1 ☆ **Read the title of the article and look at the photos. Is the article about ... ?**

- **a** new technology that is only for very rich people
- **b** new technology that everybody can use
- **c** something you see in films about the future

2 ☆☆ 🔊16 **Read and listen to the text and check your answer in exercise 1.**

▶ **Subskill: Reading for specific information**

Before you read, think of words you think are in the text, to help you look.

3 ☆☆ **Read the questions. Before you look for the answers in the text, underline the key words in the questions.**

1. Do <u>children</u> use this <u>technology</u> too?
2. How much is the Echo Dot?
3. What jobs can these machines do in the home?
4. Does everybody love voice recognition machines?
5. Do teenagers use a virtual assistant?
6. Why does voice recognition technology make people less polite?

4 ☆☆ **Match a–f with the questions in exercise 3.**

- **a** control TV, turn on lights 3
- **b** Please, rude, Thank you ___
- **c** cost, cheap ___
- **d** teen(s) ___
- **e** younger ___
- **f** like, don't like ___

5 ☆☆☆ **Read the text and answer the questions in exercise 3. The answers are not in the same order as the text. Use the word clues in exercise 4 to help you find the answers.**

1 ____________________
2 ____________________
3 ____________________
4 ____________________
5 ____________________
6 ____________________

fun facts

58% of people who use voice recognition machines use them to make shopping lists!

A survey

1 ☆ **Look at the photo. Who can you see? Choose the best answer.**

a Two friends talking in the street.
b Someone asking questions to a person they don't know.

2 ☆☆ 🔊17 **Listen and choose the best summary of the conversation.**

A woman is asking questions about …

a school
b their town
c technology

▶ Subskill: Completing a table

Listen carefully: you don't hear Speaker 1 before Speaker 2, they answer the questions at the same time.

3 ☆☆☆ **Listen again and complete the table.**

Name	1 *Tom*	2
Age	3	4
Uses … more	5	6
Why it's his/ her favourite	7	8
Three things he/she uses it for	9	10

Giving instructions

1 ☆ **Order the time expressions.**

Then/Next, ___
Finally, ___
First, *1*

2 ☆☆ **Order the words to make questions.**

1 you / me / Can / show ?
Can you show me?
2 do / do / next / What / you ?
______
3 use the scanner / you / do / How ?
______

3 ☆☆☆ **Complete the dialogue with the questions and expressions in exercises 1 and 2.**

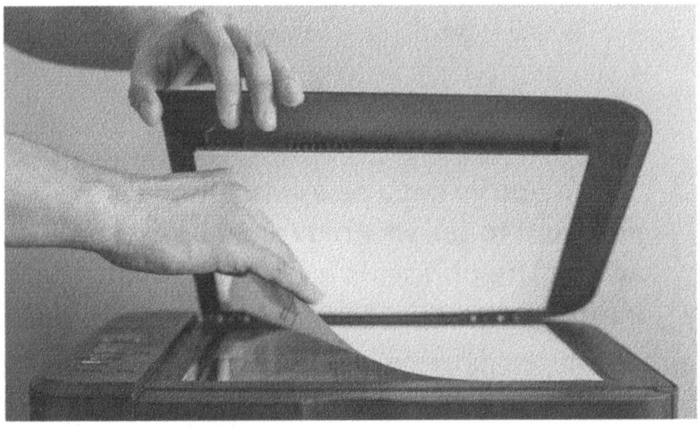

1 *How do you use the scanner?*

It's quite easy.

2 ______

Yes, no problem. 3 ______ you open it and put your document here.

OK. 4 ______

5 ______ you press this button and it starts scanning.

Right and when it finishes?

A window opens on the computer and you can see your document.

OK, I can see it.

6 ______ press 'save'.

Fantastic – thanks.

Writing

An advert

1 ☆ **Choose the correct answer.**

1	(a) quarter	b	qarter
2	a biscit	b	biscuit
3	a hoter	b	hotter
4	a interesting	b	intresting
5	a midday	b	miday
6	a stationery	b	stationry
7	a taler	b	taller
8	a sandwich	b	sanwich
9	a cleanner	b	cleaner
10	a cemist's	b	chemist's

2 ☆☆ **Match 1–5 with a–e to make sentences.**

1 This camera is perfect —— **b** for new photographers.
2 It's really
3 You can buy it
4 It's a
5 It comes with

a for only €50.
b for new photographers.
c a special bag.
d light.
e bargain!

3 ☆☆☆ **You've got a new smartphone and you want to sell your old camera. Write an advert. Use phrases in exercise 2 and other information.**

Super skills

CREATIVITY

It's important to be creative when we try to find solutions to problems.

Complete the table with the Key phrases.

Use your imagination	*4*
Listen to everyone's ideas	
Remember your ideas need to solve the problem	

1 What do you think?
2 Don't forget …
3 Let's listen to Rahul's ideas.
4 What about something really different?
5 That's an original idea!
6 Remember we need to …

Vocabulary review

Abilities

1 Which of the three sentences is not correct?

1 a I walk to school.
(b) I add a mountain.
c I tell stories to my sister.

2 a Can you spell this word?
b Can you repair my bike?
c Can you dance a plane?

3 a I can cook pasta.
b I can wash my room.
c I can climb that mountain.

4 a We play a swimming pool.
b We play the guitar.
c We play video games.

Technology nouns

2 Complete the sentences with the words in the box. There is one word you don't need.

~~camera~~	charger	keyboard
laptop	screens	touchpad

1 OK everyone, one more photo. Look at the *camera* and say 'Cheese!'.
2 This electric bicycle comes with a battery and a ______________ .
3 QWERTY are the first six letters on an English ______________ .
4 Can you close that ______________ now, please, until the plane is in the air?
5 This cinema is very big. There are ten different ______________ .

Adjectives

3 Choose the correct option.

Max: Can we take a taxi to the airport? The bus is very **1 fast/(slow)** and I don't want to walk to the bus stop, my bag is really **2 heavy/light**.

Mum: But the taxi is very **3 cheap/expensive**. We can go by train. It's **4 fast/faster** than the bus and **5 more expensive/cheaper** than the taxi. It's **6 easy/difficult** to get to the station.

Grammar review

can and *can't*

1 Complete the conversation with the correct form of *can* and the words in brackets.

Conversation 1

Jay: 1 *Can you help* **(help / you)** me with the maths homework?

Mikka: No, I **2** ________ . But Rosa **3** ________ **(help)**. She's very good at maths.

Conversation 2

Liam: Which languages **4** ________ **(speak / Mohammed)** apart from English? **5** ________ **(speak / he)** French?

Petra: **6** ________ **(speak / he)** English and Arabic, but **7** ________ **(speak / he)** French.

Comparatives

2 Write complete comparative sentences.

1 an elephant / big / a cat
An elephant is bigger than a cat.

2 Japanese / difficult / French
____

3 the bus / slow / the train
____

4 London / expensive / Liverpool
____

5 your bag / heavy / my bag
____

Possessive pronouns

3 Rewrite the sentences using possessive pronouns.

1 This is my tablet and that's his tablet.
This is mine and that's his.

2 This is our classroom and that's their classroom.
____

3 Those are her books and these are my books.
____

4 That's his chair and this is your chair.
____

Round-up 1 2 3 4 5 6 7 8

Choose the correct option.

Tech for teens

A lot of teenagers **1 love/loves** technology and we've got **2 any/some** great ideas for some cool teen tech in today's blog post.

3 Like you/Do you like sports? Our first idea is this sports smartwatch. You can check messages, listen to music and see if you can run **4 more fast/faster** than last week. **5 Can you swim/Can swim you** with this watch? Yes, **6 you swim/you can**. It's perfect for people who like water sports.

Another idea is this amazing light. **7 It's got/Has got** six different colours, so you **8 can change/can to change** the light when you want. But that's not all. It's more interesting **9 that/than** other lights. It's also a speaker, so it can light your room and play your favourite songs. **10 Is it/It is** expensive? No, it isn't. At only €35 it's **11 more cheap/cheaper** than a lot of other technology.

Self-evaluation

Read the objectives for this unit. How well can you now do each one? Put a tick (✔).

	😀	😐	🙁
1 I can talk about abilities.	☐	☐	☐
2 I can talk about technology and use adjectives to describe it.	☐	☐	☐
3 I can use *can* to talk about abilities.	☐	☐	☐
4 I can compare different things.	☐	☐	☐
5 I can read to find specific information.	☐	☐	☐
6 I can listen to complete a table.	☐	☐	☐
7 I can ask for and give instructions.	☐	☐	☐
8 I can write an advert.	☐	☐	☐

If you choose 🙁, ask your teacher for some extra help.

Grammar reference and practice pp92–93

6 The world is art

Vocabulary

Rooms and furniture; prepositions

1 ☆ **Look at the picture and write the words in the box.**

bathroom bedroom dining room ~~garden~~ hall kitchen living room

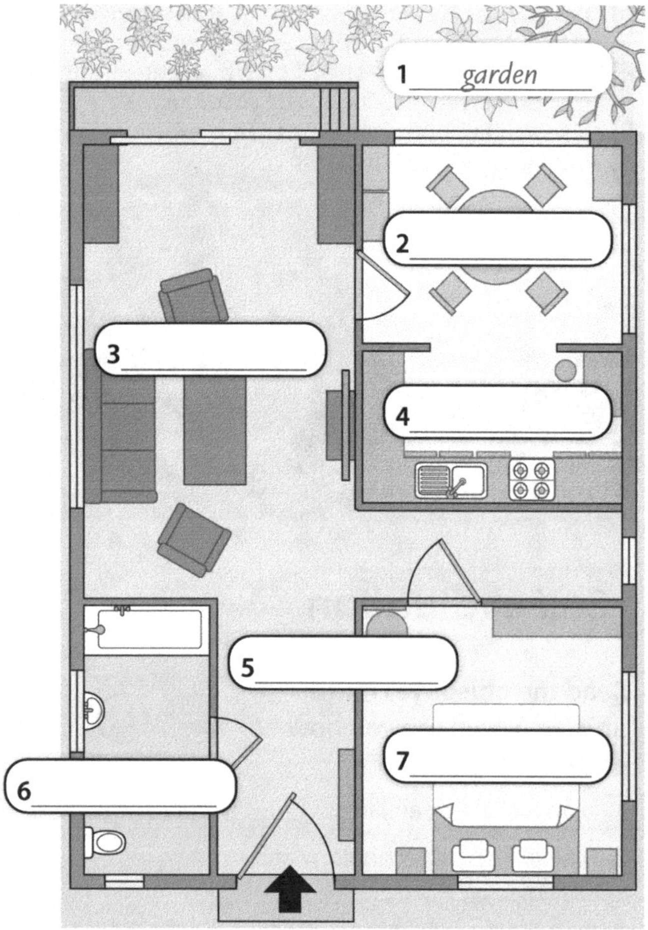

2 ☆☆ **Complete the words with the missing first letters.**

Group A

1 *b* ed
2 ___able
3 ___ath
4 ___hair
5 ___oilet
6 ___hower

Group B

1 ___all
2 ___loor
3 ___eiling

3 ☆☆ **Complete the table with the words in Group A in exercise 2.**

bedroom	bathroom	dining room
bed		

4 ☆☆ **Choose the correct option.**

This is a photo of a family **1 (in)/on** their dining room. It's breakfast time. The table is **2 above/next to** a window. Greg is **3 between/behind** his mum and dad. Greg's dad is **4 in front of/in** the window (the window is **5 in front of/behind** him). There is a bowl of fruit **6 on/under** the table, and there is some juice **7 between/under** the bowl of fruit and Greg's dad. Greg's sister, Emma, is **8 in front of/above** her dad.

5 ☆☆☆ **Write a description of your bedroom.**

____

____

____

____

____

____

____

____

Present continuous: affirmative and negative

1 ☆ **Complete the table with the *-ing* form of each verb. Be careful with the spelling.**

Infinitive	*-ing* form
start	1 *starting*
begin	2
finish	3
take	4
fly	5
add	6
chat	7
stop	8
have	9
dance	10

2 ☆ **Choose the correct answer.**

1 **(a)** They are listening to music.
  b They is listening to music.
2 **a** She not is playing tennis.
  b She isn't playing tennis.
3 **a** My brothers are siting in the car.
  b My brothers are sitting in the car.
4 **a** We aren't doing our homework.
  b We aren't do our homework.
5 **a** My mother are working.
  b My mother is working.

3 ☆☆ **Write sentences with the correct present continuous form of the verbs in brackets.**

1 Leon **(not have)** a bath. He **(have)** a shower.
Leon isn't having a bath. He's having a shower.
2 Julia and Carla **(not study)**. They **(chat)**.
______
3 We **(not watch)** a film. We **(shop)**.
______
4 Lisette **(not dance)** salsa. She **(do)** her homework.
______
5 Grant **(not read)** a book. He **(write)** a text message.
______

4 ☆☆☆ **Complete the postcard with the correct form of *be* or the *-ing* form of the verb in brackets.**

Hi Grandma,

Mum and I **1** *are* having a great time on holiday in Slovenia. We're **2** ______ **(stay)** in a town called Bled where there's a very big lake. Right now, I **3** ______ writing to you from a café. Mum **4** ______ sitting with me: she's **5** ______ **(swim)** in the lake. She's **6** ______ **(relax)** a lot: she **7** ______ working or checking her email.

We **8** ______ staying in the centre of town. We're in a small house about five kilometres from Bled. It's great, but it's quite small. Mum's got a bedroom and I'm **9** ______ **(sleep)** on a sofa-bed in the living room. I've got photos to show you when we get back home.

Lots of love,
Jack

5 ☆☆☆ **Complete the sentences. You can use your imagination if you don't know.**

1 At the moment, I ______
______.
2 My parents ______
______.
3 My teacher ______
______.
4 My best friend ______
______.

Clothes and accessories

1 ☆ **Look at the photos and write the words in the box.**

bag	dress	glasses	~~jeans~~	shoes	umbrella

1 *jeans*

2 ______

3 ______

4 ______

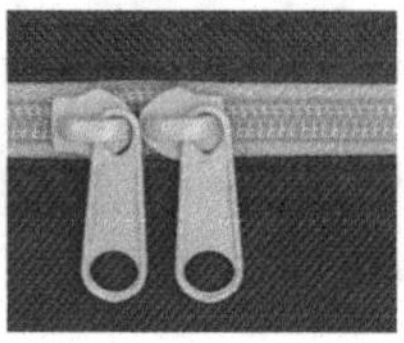

5 ______

6 ______

2 ☆☆ **Look at the photos and write the clothes and accessories. All the words start or finish with the letter *T*.**

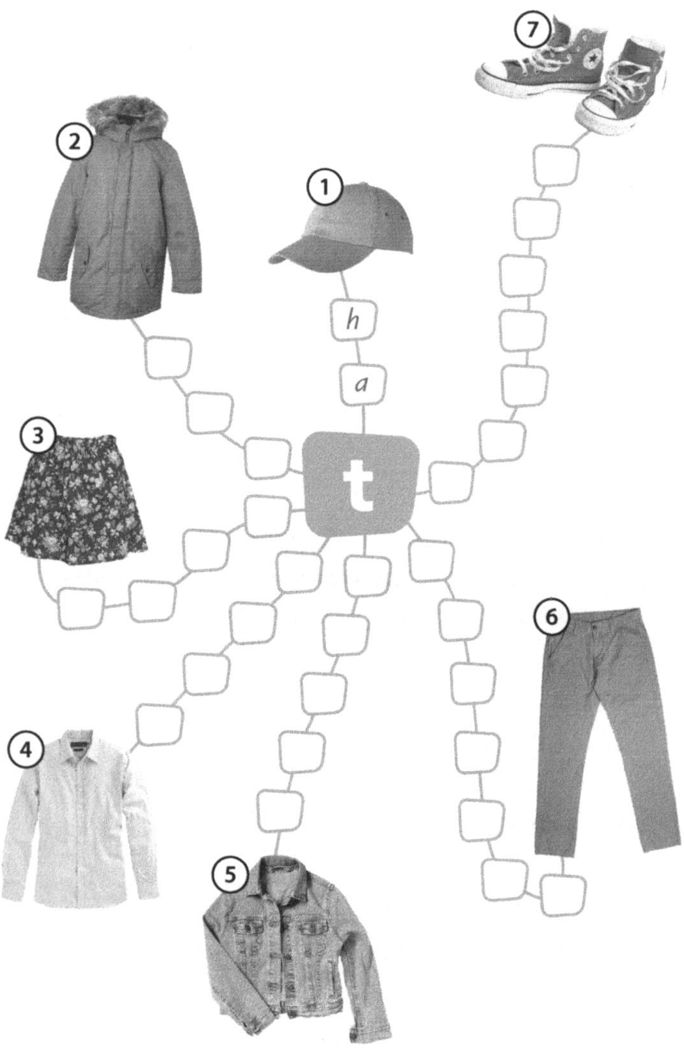

3 ☆☆ **Choose the word which is different and match it to reasons a–d.**

1	shoes	(a shirt)	trainers
2	a skirt	trousers	jeans
3	a jacket	a shirt	a coat
4	an umbrella	a skirt	trousers

a you don't wear it on top of something else ___

b you don't wear it on your feet *1*

c you don't wear it ___

d it hasn't got two legs ___

4 ☆☆ **Complete the text with the verbs *carry*, *put on*, *take off* and *wear*.**

I get up in the morning and I **1** *put on* my clothes. I have to **2** ______ a uniform to school: a black school skirt, a white shirt and a blue jacket. I've always got a lot of things to **3** ______ : my school bag, my sports bag and, on Tuesdays and Fridays, my guitar. When I come home, I **4** ______ my uniform and I **5** ______ other clothes: normally I **6** ______ jeans and a T-shirt in my free time.

5 ☆☆☆ **Answer the questions for you. What do you wear and carry … ?**

1 to school

______

2 to do sport

______

3 for a party

______

4 for a special family meal

______

Present continuous: *Yes/No* questions and short answers

1 ☆ **Order the words to make questions.**

1 walking / Are / to school / you ?
Are you walking to school?
2 his / Is / Ben / homework / doing ?
______
3 listening / me / Are / you / to ?
______
4 lunch / your / Are / friends / having ?
______
5 mum / now / Is / your / working ?
______
6 the English / Are / classroom / sitting / in / we ?
______

2 ☆☆ **Write complete *Yes/No* questions in the present continuous.**

1 students / study / English ?
Are the students studying English?
2 Zoe / sit / with Joe ?
______
3 Zoe and Joe / work / outside ?
______
4 Craig / look / at the computer screen ?
______
5 Craig / work / on a robot ?
______
6 Zoe / wear / glasses ?
______

3 ☆☆ **Look at the photo and answer the questions in exercise 2.**

1 *No, they aren't.*
2 ______
3 ______
4 ______
5 ______
6 ______

Present continuous: *Wh-* questions

4 ☆☆☆ **Complete the questions with the missing words.**

1 What *are* you doing?
2 ______ are you sitting?
3 Are you ______ to music?
4 ______ you eating anything?
5 ______ are you wearing?
6 ______ your parents working?

5 ☆☆☆ **Answer the questions in exercise 4 for you.**

1 ______
2 ______
3 ______
4 ______
5 ______
6 ______

An online article

SEE YOUR HOUSE – IN THE CINEMA!

Do you recognise the house in the first photo? It's a normal English house with a living room, three bedrooms, two bathrooms and a garden. But it's also a famous house. This is 4 Privet Drive, Surrey, the house where Harry Potter lives with his Aunt Petunia, Uncle Vernon and his cousin Dudley before he starts school at Hogwarts. It's also the house where he stays in the school holidays.

People who make films and TV programmes are always looking for houses to use. Sometimes the houses are very unusual or special, but for other films, they also want normal houses. If they make a film in your house, it is important that there is space to move. It's a good idea to ask your neighbours, too. It's very exciting when the film company first comes, but not so good if lots of noisy cars are parking in your street every week.

Another house you can see in advertisements and magazines, such as *The Times* magazine, is the home of the Milner family from Streatham, London. It's a special house and it's big, with five bedrooms, a disco room and a swimming pool in the house. People pay up to £500 a day to film in the house.

What about your home? Is it a good place to make a film or TV programme?

fun facts In the *Harry Potter* films, Hogwarts is Alnwick Castle in England. You can see it in other films, too.

1 ☆ **Look at the photos. Name all the things you can see.**

2 ☆☆ 18 **Read and listen to the text and answer the questions.**

1 Where are the two houses?

______

2 Who lives in them?

______

Subskill: Answering true or false questions

Look carefully at information in the text before you decide.

3 ☆☆☆ **Read the text again. Are the sentences T (true) or F (false)? Correct the false sentences.**

1 The house in Privet Drive has got four bedrooms.

______

2 Harry Potter lives in the house with people from his family.

______

3 After he starts at Hogwarts, he never goes back to the house.

______

4 Film makers only want special houses.

______

5 The Milner family lives in London.

______

6 They've got a swimming pool in the garden.

______

A live report

1 ☆ Look at the photo and answer the questions.

1 Where are the people?

____

2 What are they doing?

____

3 How do they feel?

____

▶ Subskill: Using photo captions to help you understand

Always look at the words in photo captions. When you listen, you can sometimes hear them.

2 ☆☆ Use a dictionary to check any words you don't know. Which caption matches the photo in exercise 1?

1 It's mine! Some people fight about special offers. ___
2 Some people prefer to stay at home. ___
3 Black Friday race? People run to start shopping. ___

3 ☆☆ Read the text and choose the correct answer.

Black Friday is a day all the listeners love. Reporter Brett Jackson is in Manchester with a live report. It's half past eight and the shops open in 15 minutes. Brett speaks with some people in the crowd. First, he talks to a woman called Shirley who wants to buy a TV. Then, he talks to a man called Joseph who prefers shopping online. Finally, the people count from one to ten and the shop opens.

1 Who is Brett Jackson?
 a a shopper **b** a reporter
2 Where is he?
 a in the radio studio **b** at the shops
3 Who is he speaking to?
 a shoppers
 b people who work in shops

4 ☆☆ 🔊19 Listen to a radio programme and find the mistakes in the text in exercise 3.

5 ☆☆☆ Listen again and correct the mistakes.

Asking for information

1 ☆ Write A if the expression is asking for information and G if the expression is giving information.

1 I'd like some information about (…) *A*
2 It costs (…) ___
3 Where's that? ___
4 What time is it open? ___
5 Can I help you? ___
6 It's open from (…:) to (…) ___
7 How much does it cost? ___
8 How can I get there? ___
9 It's at the Arts Centre. ___

2 ☆☆ Complete the dialogue with the phrases in the box.

How can I get there? How much does it cost? What time is it open? Where's that? ~~Yes, please. I'd like some information about this photography exhibition.~~

Can I help you?

1 *Yes, please. I'd like some information about this photography exhibition.*

It's at the Arts Centre.

2 ______________________

In Kinson.

3 ______________________

Take the number 3 bus.

4 ______________________

It's open from 10:00 am to 6:00 pm.

5 ______________________

Two pounds for adults and free for under 18s.

6 Writing

Text messages

1 ☆ Add *so* in the correct position in each sentence.

1 My cousin's a vegetarian *so* he doesn't eat meat.
2 I've got lots of homework today I can't go out.
3 We've got an important match on Saturday we've got extra training tonight.
4 You're free today you can help your grandmother.
5 There's a party after school I'm wearing my new jeans.
6 It's very hot today please wear a hat.

2 ☆☆ Put the text messages in the correct order.

a What about after dinner? About 7:30 pm? ___
b Hi. R U free? Do you want to come round to my house? *1*
c OK great – C U later. ___
d No, sorry. We're having dinner so I can't come now. ___
e Yes, that's fine. ___

3 ☆☆☆ Write a text conversation. Use three of the words in the box.

fine	free	great	I'm	so	sorry

Super skills

COMMUNICATION

SUPER SKILLS

It's important to communicate clearly, so everyone understands what you say.

What can you say for each of these problems? Choose the correct answers.

1 Your partner is speaking too quickly.
a That's very fast.
b That's very slow.

2 Your partner is speaking very quietly.
a Try to speak higher.
b Try to speak more loudly.

3 Your partner is looking at his/her notes all the time.
a Look up.
b Look down.

6

Vocabulary review

Rooms and furniture

1 The rooms are in the wrong sentence. Correct the sentences.

1 There's a toilet in the ~~kitchen~~. *bathroom*
2 There are two beds in my garden. ______
3 Dad's cooking lunch in the living room. ______
4 My grandmother's got a big table where we eat in her bathroom. ______
5 On hot days, we cook on a barbecue in the bedroom. ______
6 Our big TV is in the hall. ______

Prepositions

2 Choose the correct option.

1 There's a shower **above**/**under** the bath. (above circled)
2 My brother's sitting **on/in** the car.
3 Can you see my pen? It's **under/between** the chair.
4 I can't see. You're standing **in front of/behind** the TV.
5 Where's the cinema? **Above/Between** the station and the school.
6 José is sitting **on/in** his bike.

Clothes and accessories

3 Complete the sentences with the words in the box.

~~a coat~~	an umbrella	dress
glasses	trainers	trousers

1 It's cold today. Wear *a coat*.
2 We can't wear jeans at school. We have to wear ______.
3 It's raining so take ______.
4 My grandfather can't see well, so he's got ______.
5 I've got sports practice after school, so I've got my ______ in my bag.
6 Lupita Nyong'o always wears a beautiful ______ to the Oscars.

Grammar review

Present continuous: affirmative and negative

1 Complete the dialogue with the present continuous form of the verbs in brackets.

Dad: Where's Sophie?

Mum: She **1** *'s working* **(work +)** in her bedroom. She **2** ______ **(study +)** for an exam they've got tomorrow.

Dad: No, she isn't. Her phone **3** ______ **(ring +)** in her bedroom and she **4** ______ **(sit –)** at her table.

Sister: She **5** ______ **(study –)** now, she **6** ______ **(have +)** a shower.

Present continuous: *Yes/No* questions and short answers

2 Write complete questions and answers.

1 Max / repair his bike ? (✗)
Is Max repairing his bike?
No, he isn't.

2 Britta and Steffi / make lunch ? (✗)
______

3 Your teacher / correct homework ? (✔)
______

4 You and your friend / having dinner ? (✗)
______

5 Claudia / talk to Anton ? (✗)
______

Present continuous: *Wh-* questions

3 Write complete *Wh-* questions.

Greg: Today, students in Year 7 are having a fashion show. We're talking to Tania Moore about it.

Greg: 1 *Why are you having* ______?
(Why / you / have a fashion show)

Tania: To get money for our end of year party.

Greg: 2 ______?
(Where / you / do the show)

Tania: In the school gym.

Greg: 3 ______?
(What / your classmates / do)

Tania: Year 7 students Amber, Jackson and Vera are modelling clothes.

Greg: 4 ______?
(What / Amber / wear)

Tania: She's wearing a white T-shirt and trousers.

Round-up 1 2 3 4 5 6 7 8

Choose the correct option.

1 Has got your school/Has your school got a uniform? **2 Wear you/Do you wear** uniform to school? For more than 20% of students in American public schools, the answer **3 is/are** yes. Some people think it is **4 more good/better** to have a school uniform: all the students **5 wear/wears** the same clothes and you can't see **6 any/some** differences between **7 more rich/richer** and poorer children. Other people **8 don't like/like not** uniform. They like different students to wear different clothes.

In North Carolina, students from three high schools **9 are deciding/is deciding** about school uniform. The students **10 aren't making/don't making** the uniforms, but they are working with designers to learn about clothes and the cost of making uniforms. A group from each school **11 are designing/is designing** clothes they think their friends want to wear.

Self-evaluation

Read the objectives for this unit. How well can you now do each one? Put a tick (✔).

	😀	😐	🙁
1 I can talk about rooms and furniture.	☐	☐	☐
2 I can talk about clothes and accessories.	☐	☐	☐
3 I can use the present continuous to talk about things happening now.	☐	☐	☐
4 I can read a text and answer true or false questions.	☐	☐	☐
5 I can use captions to help when listening.	☐	☐	☐
6 I can ask for and give information.	☐	☐	☐
7 I can write text messages.	☐	☐	☐

If you choose 🙁, ask your teacher for some extra help.

7 Famous lives

Vocabulary

Jobs; dates

1 ☆ Complete the crossword.

Across

1 I bring food in a restaurant.
4 I correct homework.
5 I work in a hospital.
6 You can listen to me on the radio.
8 I travel in space.
9 You see me on TV and in films.

Down

2 I have ideas for new things.
3 You can see my work in a museum.
7 I don't work in the city.
10 I work in a kitchen.

2 ☆☆ Write the missing months.

January ______ March
______ May ______
July ______ September
______ ______ December

3 ☆☆ Write ordinal numbers.

1 one *first*
2 two ______
3 three ______
4 seven ______
5 eight ______
6 ten ______
7 twelve ______
8 fifteen ______
9 nineteen ______
10 twenty-one ______
11 twenty-six ______
12 thirty ______

4 ☆☆ Write the birthdays of the actors in words.

Mavrick Moreno 30.01
1 *The thirtieth of January*

Elle Fanning 09.04
2 ______

Caleb McLaughlin 13.10
3 ______

Amandla Stenberg 23.10
4 ______

Kiernan Shipka 10.11
5 ______

Lucas Hedges 12.12
6 ______

5 ☆☆☆ Write five dates that are important for you and say why.

1 ______
2 ______
3 ______
4 ______
5 ______

Past simple of *be:* affirmative and negative

1 ☆ **Complete the sentences with *was* or *were*.**

1 Lin and Ross ___*were*___ at the cinema.
2 Sophie and I ______ at a party.
3 Uncle Billy ______ at the swimming pool.
4 My parents ______ at a restaurant.
5 Grandma ______ at the supermarket.

2 ☆☆ **Complete the text with *was, were, wasn't* or *weren't*.**

FANNY CRADOCK: TV COOK

Today there are lots of programmes on TV about cooking, with competitions like *Masterchef* and famous TV cooks, but Fanny Cradock **1** ___*was*___ **(+)** the first TV cook in the UK. Fanny **2** ______ **(+)** from London, but her real name **3** ______ **(–)** Fanny; it was Phyllis.

Fanny's first programme **4** ______ **(+)** in 1955. Fanny and her husband Johnny **5** ______ **(+)** both on the programme. The Cradocks **6** ______ **(–)** only famous because of TV, but because of a regular article in the *Daily Telegraph* newspaper.

Fanny **7** ______ **(–)** always popular, but she **8** ______ **(+)** a very famous name in Britain.

Past simple of *be*: *Yes/No* questions and short answers

3 ☆☆ **The police are asking questions to a suspect. Add the missing words to each question.**

1 were at the cinema yesterday? **(you)**
Were you at the cinema yesterday?
2 it the MultiScreen Cinema? **(was)**
______
3 were you with? **(another person)**
______
4 was *Star City*? **(the film)**
______
5 the film at 4:00 pm? **(was)**
______
6 were you in row 6? **(and your friend)**
______

4 ☆☆ **Look at the tickets and write short answers to the questions in exercise 3.**

1 *Yes, I was.*
2 ______
3 ______
4 ______
5 ______
6 ______

Past simple of *be*: *Wh-* questions

5 ☆☆☆ **Write questions in the past simple about the underlined words.**

1 My best friend's name was Nicky.
What was your best friend's name?
2 My school was in Norwood.
______
3 My mother was 39 years old.
______
4 My favourite food was pasta.
______
5 My bedtime was at half past eight.
______
6 My favourite TV programme was *Dora the Explorer*.
______

6 ☆☆☆ **Write your answers to the questions in exercise 5 about when you were six. Include extra information.**

1 ______
2 ______
3 ______
4 ______
5 ______
6 ______

Adjectives to describe feelings

1 ☆ 20 **Listen and complete the table with the words in the box, according to the pronunciation (O = stressed syllable).**

~~afraid~~ ~~bored~~ ~~hungry~~ ill pleased relaxed surprised thirsty tired well worried

O	Oo	oO
bored	*hungry*	*afraid*

2 ☆☆ **Complete the crossword with the correct adjectives. What is the adjective in the grey line?**

1 I feel hot and cold and I don't feel good. I think I'm … .
2 When you want to eat, you're … .
3 When you want to drink, you're … .
4 The opposite of ill is … .
5 Dad always gets home at 6:00. It's now 8:00 and he's not here. I'm … .
6 I got a good mark in my exam. I'm very … .
7 My friend was on the bus this morning, but he usually goes to school by car. I was … .
8 I was at the gym all morning and now I feel very … .
9 At the end of the school holidays, after six weeks of no work, I feel very … .
10 This film isn't interesting. I'm very … .

3 ☆☆ **Tick (✔) the correct sentences.**

1 When I see a big dog, I feel thirsty. ☐
2 If you eat something bad, you can get relaxed. ☐
3 My breakfast was very small today. I'm feeling hungry. ☐
4 I was surprised to see our maths teacher in the supermarket on Saturday. ☐
5 James loves history so he was very worried in the Roman Museum. ☐
6 You're very late home. I was tired about you. ☐

4 ☆☆ **Correct the incorrect sentences in exercise 3.**

When I see a big dog, I feel afraid.

5 ☆☆☆ **Choose five adjectives and write about a situation when you have each feeling.**

1
2
3
4
5

Past simple of regular verbs: affirmative

1 ☆ **Write the past simple of the verbs in the box.**

~~ask~~ change dance end listen plan stay travel try work

asked

2 ☆☆ **Read about Louise's typical Friday afternoon. Then write what she did last Friday.**

On Fridays, she walks home from school and changes her clothes. Then she starts her homework. She studies for about two hours and she stops doing her homework at about eight o'clock.

When she finishes, she calls her friend and they chat for about 20 minutes. They decide what to do on Saturday. Then Louise watches a series until it's time for bed.

Last Friday, she walked home from school and ...

Past simple of irregular verbs: affirmative

3 ☆☆ **Complete the table.**

Infinitive	Past simple
have	1 *had*
2	won
3	got
leave	4
be	5
6	met
take	7
tell	8
9	wore
10	wrote

4 ☆☆☆ **Complete the text with the past simple form of the verbs in brackets.**

Last week, my friend **1** *told* **(tell)** me about Sky Brown and yesterday I **2** ______ **(see)** a video of her. Sky is a world champion skateboarder, but she's only 11. On the video, she **3** ______ **(do)** some amazing tricks. Sky is half Japanese and half British, and last year she **4** ______ **(become)** part of the British national team. She wants to go to the Olympics. Sky **5** ______ **(begin)** skateboarding when she **6** ______ **(be)** three. But Sky doesn't only do skateboarding. She's an excellent surfer and when she **7** ______ **(go)** on the TV competition *Dancing with the Stars: Juniors* in the USA, she **8** ______ **(win)** it!

5 ☆☆☆ **Answer the questions for you.**

1 What did you do at the weekend?

2 What did you do for your last birthday?

3 What did you do on your last holiday?

7 Reading

A biography

An influential* teenager

Marley Dias was born on 3rd January 2005 in Philadelphia, in the United States. Her family comes from Jamaica and Cape Verde, but Marley lives in New Jersey.

Marley loves books and reading, but when she was in 6th grade, she noticed something. In the books she read at school, the main character was always a white boy. Where were the black girls? Marley went home and told her mother about it. Marley decided to do something about the problem. In 2015, she started a programme called *1000 Black Girl Books*. Marley wanted to get books with black girls as the main character. In the end, she got 11,000 books and gave them to schools and libraries in the USA and in other countries, too.

But there is still a problem. In 2016, there were 3,400 new books in the USA, but only 8.4% of the books had a main character who was African-American. Marley started speaking about the problem and people began to listen to her. She was on TV and she visited the White House. People said she was one of the most influential young people in the USA.

Marley thinks young people can change things, and in 2019 she wrote a book about it: *Marley Dias Gets It Done: And So Can You*.

*an influential person makes other people change what they think and do

fun facts Ms Marvel (Kamala Khan) is a Pakistani-American superhero. She can extend her arms and legs so they are very long, and change her appearance.

1 ☆ **Answer the questions for you.**

1 What are three of your favourite books?

______

______

______

2 Which reasons are important when you choose a book?

☐ I like the main character.

☐ I like the type of book.

☐ A friend read it and liked it.

2 ☆☆ 21 **Read and listen to the text and choose the best summary.**

a Marley Dias loves reading.

b Marley Dias saw a problem and did something about it.

c Marley Dias wrote a book about a problem.

▶ Subskill: Reading in different ways

Move your eyes quickly over the text to find specific words. When you find them, read closely and intensively to check.

3 ☆☆☆ **Read the text again and choose the correct option.**

1 Marley was born in **2003/2005/2015**.

2 Marley is from **Jamaica/Cape Verde/The USA**.

3 Marley was angry because there were no books about **black boys/white girls/black girls**.

4 She started *1000 Black Girl Books* in **2016/2015/2019**.

5 She got **11,000/1,000/10,000** books.

6 In 2016, **not many/some/a lot of** books had African-American main characters.

7 Marley **was in a film/wrote a book/had a TV show**.

4 ☆☆☆ **Answer the questions.**

1 What month was Marley born?

January

2 Where does she live?

______

3 Who did Marley tell about the problem?

______

4 What did Marley do with the books she got?

______

5 What special place did Marley visit?

______

6 What is the name of Marley's book?

______

A discussion

1 ☆ **Complete the table with the famous people in the box.**

~~Adele~~ Beyoncé Bruno Mars Emma Gonzalez Greta Thunberg Leo Messi Malala Yousafzai Roger Federer Serena Williams Simone Biles Taylor Swift Usain Bolt

Music	*Adele*
Sport	
Not music or sport	

2 ☆ **Add people from your country to the three categories.**

3 ☆☆ 🔊22 **Listen to the conversation. Which people in exercise 1 don't they name?**

____

____

____

Subskill: Matching speakers with what they say

Read all the sentences first before you listen to match speakers with what they say. Remember, the order of the sentences is not the same as on the audio.

4 ☆☆☆ **Listen again and write who says each thing: Claire (C), Alfie (A) or both Claire and Alfie (B).**

1 It's difficult to compare people from music and sport. *A*
2 A football player was the best sports person. ___
3 Two tennis players were the best sports people. ___
4 Adele was the best singer. ___
5 Beyoncé was the best singer. ___
6 Greta Thunberg was the most important person. ___

Talking about last weekend

1 ☆ **Complete the phrases with the words in the box.**

fun morning Saturday thanks time ~~weekend~~ you

1 How was your *weekend* ?
2 What about in the ___________ ?
3 Was it ___________ ?
4 What about ___________ ?
5 It was brilliant, ___________ .
6 I had a great ___________ !
7 What about ___________ ?

2 ☆☆ **Complete the conversation with some of the questions in exercise 1.**

Jacob: 1 *How was your weekend* ?
Lee: It was great, thanks. On Friday evening, I went to Sara's house.
Jacob: 2 ___________ ?
Lee: On Saturday morning, I had volleyball practice and in the evening I went to Lucy's party.
Jacob: 3 ___________ ?
Lee: Yes, it was brilliant.
Jacob: And Sunday?
Lee: It was OK. I got up late and then I did my homework. **4** ___________ ?

A description of a fictional character

1 ☆ **Add *also* in the correct position in each sentence.**

1 She loves reading and she *also* writes stories.
2 He's good at English and he's good at maths.
3 Jake's good at repairing computers and he can build robots.
4 He was born in Peru so he speaks Spanish.
5 Kim and Shayla were at the party.
6 We went to Malaysia and we visited Singapore.

2 ☆☆ **Tick (✔) the things you usually include in a description of a character in a TV series.**

1 the name of the character ☐
2 the name of the series ☐
3 a description of the character ☐
4 a description of all the other characters in the series ☐
5 information about the character's family and early life ☐
6 why they are important in the story ☐
7 why you like this character ☐
8 information about when and where you watch this programme ☐

3 ☆☆☆ **Write a description of a character from a TV series.**

Super skills

COLLABORATION

SUPER SKILLS

When you decide what information to include in a project, you do a lot of research first.

Which expressions (a–d) do we use to do 1 and 2?

1 Talk through all your ideas before you decide. *a* ___
2 Include surprising or interesting information. ___ ___

a OK, so what information have we got?
b (…) is very important. It was new for me.
c This is very interesting.
d Is there any more information?

Vocabulary review

Jobs

1 Write the jobs.

1 I work in a kitchen. *cook*
2 I work in a hospital. ______
3 I spend my day outside with animals. ______
4 I carry food and drinks. ______
5 I have ideas and make new things. ______
6 I work in films and on TV. ______

Dates

2 Complete the table.

27.05	1 *the twenty-seventh of May*
2	the twelfth of March
23.10	3
4	the tenth of June
02.11	5
6	the fifteenth of July
01.08	7
8	the thirteenth of February

Adjectives to describe feelings

3 Complete the conversation with adjectives.

Rani: Do you want anything to eat?
Misha: No, thanks. I'm not **1** *hungry*.
Rani: Are you OK? You look **2** ______.
Misha: No, I'm very hot and I don't feel **3** ______.
Rani: Have some water – it's important to drink.
Misha: OK, good idea. I am feeling a bit **4** ______.
Rani: Why don't you go to bed and sleep for a bit?
Misha: Yes, good idea. I'm very **5** ______.

Grammar review

Past simple of *be*

1 Choose the correct option.

Hi Beth,

Sorry I **1 wasn't/was** free to talk yesterday. It **2 were/was** my grandmother's birthday and we **3 were/was** at her house. It **4 wasn't/was** a special party because she **5 was/were** 70. My brother and sister **6 was/were** there too, but my cousins **7 wasn't/weren't** at the party.

How **8 was/were** your tennis match? I want to hear all about it.

Talk soon,
Christie

Past simple of regular verbs: affirmative

2 Complete the sentences with the past simple form of the verbs in brackets. Decide which verb comes first.

1 School *started* late yesterday, so I *stayed* in bed till 9:30. **(stay/start)**

2 Mum ________ me and ________ me to make the dinner. **(ask/call)**

3 I ________ that book, but I can't remember how it ________. **(enjoy/end)**

4 We ________ to go by bus, but in the end we ________. **(plan/walk)**

5 We've got an exam, so I ________ watching TV and ________. **(study/stop)**

Past simple of irregular verbs: affirmative

3 Complete the text with the past form of the irregular and regular verbs in brackets.

Cameron Davis is 13 and his family loves travelling. When Cameron **1** *was* **(be)** five, his family **2** ________ **(go)** to Peru and when he was six, they **3** ________ **(start)** a trip round the world. In one year, they **4** ________ **(visit)** 29 countries. Cameron **5** ________ **(miss)** 2nd grade in school, but he **6** ________ **(study)** online and he **7** ________ **(have)** a lot of amazing experiences: he **8** ________ **(go)** mountain-biking in Canada, he **9** ________ **(eat)** curry in India and he **10** ________ **(make)** lots of new friends.

Round-up 1 2 3 4 5 6 7 8

Choose the correct option.

Sisters make a difference

When sisters Melati and Isabel Wijsen **1 was/were** in school one day, they **2 have/had** a lesson about people who made a difference, like Gandhi and Nelson Mandela.

The girls **3 are/is** from the island of Bali in Indonesia. In Bali, there **4 are/is** a big problem: there is **5 any/a lot of** plastic, especially in the sea. Melati and Isabel **6 did see/saw** it every time they went swimming. So they decided to start **7 an/a** organisation called Bye Bye Plastic Bags (BBPB). Melati didn't want to wait until they were **8 older/more old**. They also organised an event to clean Bali's beaches with over 12,000 people.

Now, their organisation **9 getting/is getting** bigger. The girls **10 speaks/speak** to children in schools, meet politicians and give TED talks, and **11 are there/there are** now 50 BBPB teams around the world.

Self-evaluation

Read the objectives for this unit. How well can you now do each one? Put a tick (✔).

1 I can talk about jobs and dates.

2 I can use adjectives to describe feelings.

3 I can use the past simple to talk about things that happened in the past.

4 I can read in different ways to find information.

5 I can identify what different people say.

6 I can ask about last weekend.

7 I can write a description of a character in a TV series.

If you choose ☹, ask your teacher for some extra help.

8 From A to B

Vocabulary

Transport

1 ☆ **Complete the types of transport with the missing letters.**

1 c *a* r
2 b __ s
3 b __ k __
4 t __ x __
5 b __ __ t
6 tr __ __ n
7 pl __ n __

2 ☆☆ **Which form of transport in each group does *not* fit in the group?**

1 You travel with other people:
a boat (**b**) bike **c** bus
2 It's good for a journey of 200 km:
a plane **b** train **c** on foot
3 It's a form of public transport:
a bus **b** car **c** train
4 It's got doors:
a bike **b** plane **c** taxi
5 You travel by road:
a boat **b** taxi **c** bus

3 ☆☆ **Find eight forms of transport and three people connected with travelling in the word square.**

(D	R	I	V	E	R)	P	A	B	L
C	O	A	C	H	G	I	H	I	O
C	D	M	E	F	M	L	J	K	R
L	M	B	S	C	O	O	T	E	R
N	O	U	P	Q	T	T	R	S	Y
H	E	L	I	C	O	P	T	E	R
T	U	A	V	W	R	X	R	Y	Z
A	C	N	D	E	B	F	A	G	H
B	L	C	S	H	I	P	M	K	I
M	N	E	O	O	K	P	Q	J	R
S	P	A	S	S	E	N	G	E	R

4 ☆☆ **Complete the sentences with forms of transport.**

1 They took my grandmother to hospital by *ambulance*, but she went home the same day.
2 Three walkers were lost in the mountains, but a ______________ flew to rescue them.
3 New York and Paris both have an ______________ : the Subway in New York and the Metro in Paris.
4 My brother wants to get a ______________, but my parents say it's too dangerous on the roads.
5 When we moved house last summer, a big ______________ moved all our furniture.
6 By ______________, it takes about six hours from the UK to the USA, but by ______________, it can take a week.

5 ☆☆☆ **Answer the questions for you.**

1 How do you normally travel in your city?
____
2 How did you travel last time you went on holiday?
____
3 How do people from your city travel to the capital of your country (or another big city if you live in the capital)?
____
4 Which do you prefer: travelling by coach or travelling by train? Why?
____
____

Past simple: negative

1 ☆ **Tick (✔) the three sentences that are correct. Correct the mistakes in the other sentences.**

Kev: What was our English homework? ✔
Alex: I not write it in my notebook. ☐
Joe: We've got the maths test today because we didn't have it yesterday. ☐
Sam: Oh no! I studied not for it. ☐
Paula: I'm hungry – I didn't have time for breakfast. ☐
Kev: Where's Jude? I don't see her on the bus. ☐
Vicky: She didn't took the bus today, she came by train. ☐

Alex: I didn't write it in my notebook.

____

____

____

2 ☆☆ **Complete the sentences with the past simple negative form of the verbs in the box.**

buy go have start ~~take~~ watch

1 The traffic was very bad, so we *didn't take* the bus.
2 They decided to walk home because Rishi ______________ a travel card.
3 It was a bit cold, so we ______________ to the beach.
4 I don't like rugby, so I ______________ the match last night.
5 Everything in the games shop was very expensive, so we ______________ anything.
6 The film ______________ at 8:00 pm, it began at 7:30 pm.

Past simple: questions and short answers

3 ☆☆ **Write complete questions with the past simple.**

1 Henry Ford and Karl Benz both / make cars ?
Did Henry Ford and Karl Benz both make cars?
2 Ford's Model T cars / come in many colours ?
____
3 cars / become popular quickly / in the USA ?
____
4 Moulton Taylor / invent / the racing car ?
____
5 Harry Potter and Ron / travel / on a flying bicycle ?
____
6 James Bond / drive / an Aston Martin ?
____

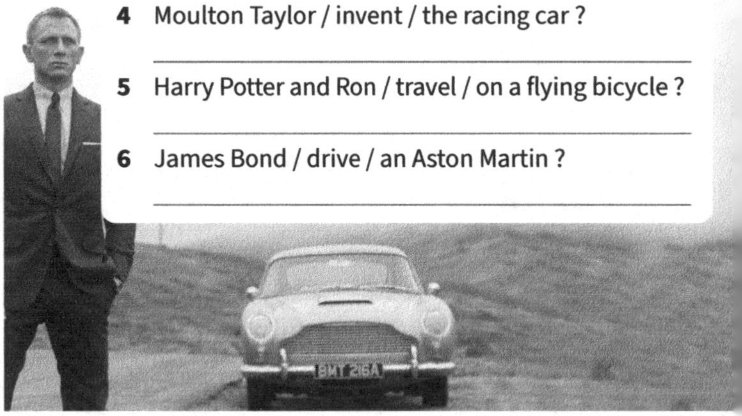

4 ☆☆ **Write short answers for the questions.**

1 (+) *Yes, they did*. Benz made the first car, but Ford's was more popular.
2 (–) ______________. They were only black.
3 (+) ______________. In 1920, there were eight million cars.
4 (–) ______________. He invented the first flying car in 1956.
5 (–) ______________. They travelled in a flying car.
6 (+) ______________. He drove an Aston Martin DB5.

5 ☆☆☆ **Complete the questions with the verbs in the box.**

do get ~~go~~ see

Angus: I had a lovely day in Manchester last week.
Gordon: **1** Who *did you go* with?
Angus: My aunt and my cousin Jo.
Gordon: **2** What ______________?
Angus: We went shopping and then we went to the cinema.
Gordon: **3** What ______________?
Angus: The latest *Mission Impossible* film. It was great.
Gordon: **4** What time ______________ home?
Angus: We weren't back till late – about 10:00 pm.

6 ☆☆☆ **Write a conversation about a day out you had.**

Grammar reference and practice pp98–99

Transport collocations

1 ☆ **Choose the answer which is incorrect.**

1 buy
a a ticket (b) a queue c a travel card
2 take
a a taxi b a plane c a foot
3 ride
a a car b a horse c a motorbike
4 a get into b get on c get out of
a car
5 go on
a foot b bike c a tour
6 a take b get on c wait
a bus

2 ☆ **Look at the photos and write phrases in exercise 1.**

1 
go on foot

2 
____

3 
____

4 
____

5 
____

6 
____

3 ☆☆ **Put the steps of a bus journey in the correct order.**

a ring the bell ___
b get on the bus ___
c wait in a queue *1*
d get off the bus ___
e buy a ticket ___

4 ☆☆ **Choose the correct answer.**

1 We were late for our plane, so we decided to …
a ride a bike (b) take a taxi
2 It isn't a direct line. You have to …
a change trains b wait in a queue
3 The traffic in the town centre is terrible. It's quicker to …
a go on foot b go by bus
4 Remember to look both ways before you …
a ring the bell b cross the road
5 We didn't know Manchester, so we decided to …
a go on a tour b buy a ticket

5 ☆☆ **Complete the table with irregular transport verbs.**

Infinitive	Past simple
buy	1 *bought*
2	drove
get	3
go	4
5	rode
6	rang
take	7

6 ☆☆☆ **Complete the text with words in exercise 5.**

Last year we went to see my friend in France. I **1** *took* a plane to Paris with my mum. My mum **2** ______ our tickets online, and she **3** ______ us to the airport in the car. The holiday was great, we **4** ______ bikes in the countryside most days, but my favourite was the day we **5** ______ on a tour of Paris! I can't wait to go again next year.

7 ☆☆☆ **Write a description of a difficult journey you had.**

Superlative adjectives

1 ☆ Write the superlative of the adjectives.

1 tall *the tallest*
2 happy ______
3 interesting ______
4 fast ______
5 nice ______
6 bad ______
7 hot ______
8 good ______
9 difficult ______
10 easy ______

2 ☆☆ Complete Sonia's summary with superlative adjectives in exercise 1.

Subjects:
interesting – technology
easy – art
difficult – maths

Day:
Tuesday ✔ ✔ ✔
Thursday ☹☹☹

Teachers:
nice Mrs Fox ✔ ✔ ✔

Here are the results of our class questionnaire.

Most students in the class think that …

1 technology is *the most interesting* subject.
2 art is ______ subject.
3 maths is ______ subject.
4 Tuesday is ______ day of the week.
5 Thursday is ______ day of the week.
6 Mrs Fox is ______ teacher.

3 ☆☆ Complete the text with the superlative forms of the adjectives in brackets.

Around the world – underground

The London Underground is the **1** *oldest* **(old)** system in the world and it probably has the **2** ______ **(famous)** underground map, but did you know that London also has the world's **3** ______ **(expensive)** public transport system?

Tokyo has the **4** ______ **(busy)** underground system in the world. One of the **5** ______ **(big)** systems is Beijing's metro, but New York has got more stations. At the opposite end, Carmelit in Israel is one of the **6** ______ **(small)** underground systems with only one 1.8 km tunnel.

People say Moscow has the **7** ______ **(good)** underground system.

4 ☆☆☆ Write complete sentences using comparative and superlative forms.

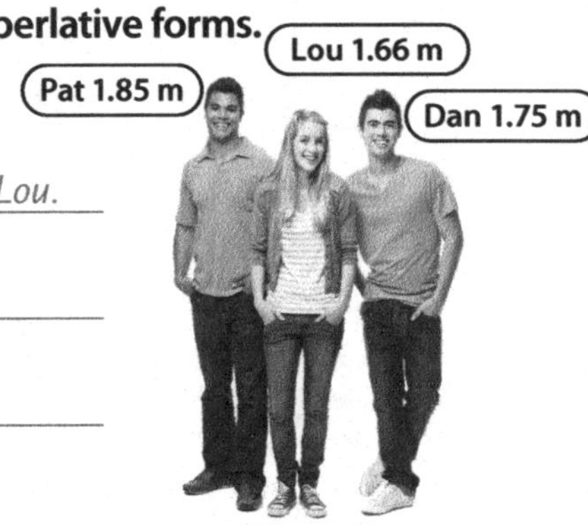

1 tall/short
(Dan / Lou)
Dan is taller than Lou.
(Lou)
Lou is the shortest.
(Pat)
Pat is the tallest.

2 expensive/cheap
(trousers / T-shirt)
______
(jacket)
______
(T-shirt)
______

3 quick/slow
(car / bus)
______
(bus)
______
(train)
______

5 ☆☆☆ Complete the questions with superlatives and answer for you.

1 What's *the best* **(good)** place to go shopping in your city?
______
2 What's ______ **(dangerous)** sport?
______
3 What's ______ **(interesting)** way to travel?
______

An article about technology

> **fun facts** Canada is looking at another type of fast train. The journey from Toronto to Vancouver now takes three days by train, but with the new train it could take just three hours!

Meet the Maglev

1 *What is the Maglev?*

The Maglev is the world's fastest train. The word *maglev* comes from *magnetic* levitation*, a new type of train technology. In tests in Japan in 2015, the Maglev travelled at 600 kilometres per hour.

2 ______

The Maglev is very popular in Asia. China, Japan and South Korea all have Maglev trains. One of the most popular is the Shanghai Maglev. It takes an hour to get to Shanghai airport by taxi but only eight minutes by Maglev.

3 ______

The Maglev isn't very popular in Europe. Birmingham Airport in the UK had a Maglev for 11 years but closed it because it was too expensive.

4 ______

The main advantage is that it's a lot quicker than a normal train. But people also say that it's safer. It's bigger too and some passengers think it's more comfortable. One of the most important advantages is that it's better for the environment. But not everyone thinks this train is great. Some people say it is very expensive to build and to repair.

5 ______

In Asia, they want to make more Maglev train lines. They are also building a new super-fast Maglev in China. They say it can travel at 1,000 kilometres per hour – that's faster than a plane!

*magnetic: able to attract metal

Subskill: Asking questions before you read

Before you read, think about what you want to know about the text.

1 ☆ **Look at the photos and choose three things from the list that you would like to know.**

1 What's the name of this train? ✔
2 How fast can the train travel? ☐
3 What countries have this train? ☐
4 How much does a ticket cost? ☐
5 Do passengers like this train? ☐
6 How does this train compare to other trains? ☐

2 ☆☆ 23 **Read and listen to the text to find the answers to your questions.**

1 *The Maglev*
2 ______
3 ______
4 ______
5 ______
6 ______

3 ☆☆☆ **Read the text again and match headings a–e with paragraphs 1–5.**

a Are there Maglevs in Europe?
b What's the future of Maglev?
c What is the Maglev?
d What are the advantages and disadvantages?
e Where can you travel by Maglev?

4 ☆☆☆ **Are the sentences T (true) or F (false)? Correct the false sentences.**

1 Maglev is a Japanese word.
F – It comes from magnetic levitation.
2 It's quicker to go to Shanghai airport by train than by car.
______
3 There is a Maglev in Birmingham.
______
4 The Maglev is more dangerous than other trains.
______
5 The Maglev is good for the environment.
______
6 The new Maglev is quicker than a plane.
______

Announcements

1 ☆ In which of the places in the box can we hear announcements?

at home	in a chemist's	in a restaurant
in a station	in an airport	

2 ☆ 24 Listen to six announcements. For each one, decide if it is for passengers travelling by plane (P), train (T) or coach (C).

1 *P* 3 ___ 5 ___
2 ___ 4 ___ 6 ___

Subskill: Listening to choose the best summary

Read the options before you listen. When listening, it's not important to understand every word.

3 ☆☆ 25 Listen and match announcements 1–5 with a–e.

Passengers …

- **a** can now get on the plane. *4*
- **b** hear information at a station about the next train. ___
- **c** hear the number of the gate a plane leaves from. ___
- **d** hear where to go to continue their journey. ___
- **e** hear a change of gate. ___

4 ☆☆☆ 26 Listen to announcement 6 and answer the questions.

1. Where is the coach going? *Manchester*
2. Do you have to pay to use Wi-Fi on this coach? ___
3. Is there a toilet? ___
4. What can't you eat on the coach? ___
5. Can you use your phone? ___
6. What time does the coach arrive in Manchester? ___

Buying a ticket

1 ☆ Complete the expressions with the words in the box.

buy	change	~~go~~	take

1. *Go* to the station.
2. ___ your ticket at the machine.
3. ___ the 2:30 train to Burnley.
4. ___ trains at Milton Keynes.

2 ☆☆ Match 1–5 with a–e to make expressions.

1. What's the
2. How much
3. Where do I
4. What time's the
5. Is that single

- **a** get the train?
- **b** next train?
- **c** fastest way to get to Dundee?
- **d** or return?
- **e** does it cost?

3 ☆☆☆ Order the sentences to make a conversation.

- **a** Thanks. What time's the next train? ___
- **b** At Paisley, change onto the airport bus. ___
- **c** Great – thank you! *9*
- **d** Excuse me, what's the fastest way to get to Glasgow Airport? *1*
- **e** Seven pounds fifty. Buy your ticket at that machine. ___
- **f** To the airport? Take the train to Paisley. ___
- **g** There's a train in five minutes. ___
- **h** Ok, how much does it cost? *5*
- **i** OK, train to Paisley, then what? ___

8 Writing

A story

1 ☆☆ **Complete the sentences with *before* or *after*.**

1 I bought a ticket *before* I got on the train.

2 ______________ I got home, I did my homework.

3 ______________ she went to bed, Leah had a bath.

4 James washed his hands ______________ he finished repairing his bike.

5 ______________ his birthday, Frankie called his grandfather to thank him for his present.

6 We studied a lot ______________ the exam.

2 ☆☆☆ **Write a story about a difficult journey. Include three of the expressions in the box.**

an accident had an exam I forgot my … my cousin's wedding nearly missed the … our car didn't start went by taxi woke up late

____

____

____

____

____

____

____

____

____

____

Super skills

COLLABORATION

SUPER SKILLS

Everyone is important in a group, but it's good to take different roles when you work together.

Match phrases 1–3 with the tips.

1 Make a list of things to do.
2 Decide who can do each thing.
3 Check to see that you divide the work equally.

a Has everyone got something to do?
b OK, so what things do we have to do?
c You're good at art. Can you make the poster?
d I can do (…) and can you do (…) ?

8

Vocabulary review

Transport

1 Complete the table with the words in the box, according to the number of wheels on each form of transport.

ambulance ~~bike~~ car helicopter lorry motorbike scooter ship taxi train

bike

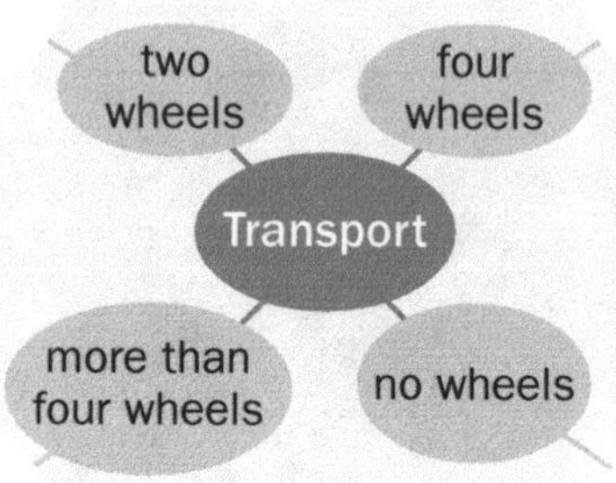

Transport collocations

2 Tick the possible combinations in the table.

	get	go	ride	take
off a bus	✔	✘	✘	✘
by car				
a plane				
a horse				
into a taxi				
a motorbike				
a train				
on foot				

3 Complete the description.

There are several different forms of transport in my city and you can **1** *buy* a young person's ticket for a month for just €20. When I go to school, I normally **2** ______________ by bus because there's a bus stop five minutes from my house. I can **3** ______________ off the bus opposite our school and I just have to **4** ______________ the road. When I meet my friends, I **5** ______________ on foot because they all live near our house. If I go to other parts of the city, I normally **6** ______________ the underground. We haven't got a car, so sometimes if I go out with my parents we **7** ______________ a taxi.

Grammar review

Past simple: negative

1 Rewrite the sentences in the negative form.

1 We went to France on holiday last year.
We didn't go to France on holiday last year.

2 I saw Tessa at school today.
____

3 The train left at 7:00.
____

4 Henry took his tablet on the plane.
____

5 Georgia and I met at my cousin's house.
____

Past simple: questions and short answers

2 Complete the questions and answers. Use the verbs in the box in the questions.

go	have	~~see~~	take

1 **Anna:** *Did you see* Gareth at your guitar lesson today?
Barney: *No, I didn't*. He's not well and he wasn't there.

2 **Luke:** ________ to the cinema?
Dinah: ________. The film was great.

3 **Laurie:** ________ the bus this morning?
Phil: ________. My mum drove me.

4 **Olivia:** ________ spaghetti at the restaurant last night?
Benny: ________. You know I love pasta!

Superlative adjectives

3 Complete the sentences with a superlative adjective.

1 It was a very cold day today. It was *the coldest day* of the year.

2 She's a very good singer. She's ________ in our class.

3 It's a dangerous part of town. I think it's ________ I know.

4 All the boxes are very heavy, but this one is ________ to carry.

5 My brother goes to a very big school. Mum says it's ________ in our part of the city.

Round-up 1 2 3 4 5 6 7 8

Choose the correct option.

NEVER TOO YOUNG TO DRIVE

1 ~~Do you think~~**/Do think you** that people can only drive when they're 18? Well, you're wrong! There are now **2 any/some** special driving schools for children and teenagers, too! One driving school **3 have got/has got** 60 centres for young drivers in the UK.

Eleven-year-old Lucy **4 had/did have** her first lesson last week. 'It was great! Before the class **5 I didn't knew/I didn't know** how to drive and at the end, I could start and stop the car and drive by myself! The **6 best/better** thing was the teacher. She explained everything very clearly.'

And if you've got a **7 younger/more young** brother or sister, they **8 can learn/can to learn** to drive, too! **9 There are/Are** classes in special cars for five- to ten-year-olds.

The schools **10 is/are** open all year with classes on Saturdays and Sundays. Lessons **11 costs/cost** £37 for a 30-minute class.

Self-evaluation

Read the objectives for this unit. How well can you now do each one? Put a tick (✔).

	😀	😐	🙁
1 I can talk about transport.	☐	☐	☐
2 I can use transport collocations.	☐	☐	☐
3 I can use the past simple negative and questions to talk about the past.	☐	☐	☐
4 I can use superlative adjectives.	☐	☐	☐
5 I can think of questions about a text before I read.	☐	☐	☐
6 I can understand transport announcements.	☐	☐	☐
7 I can ask for information about a journey.	☐	☐	☐
8 I can write a story.	☐	☐	☐

If you choose 🙁, ask your teacher for some extra help.

9 Look what you know!

Vocabulary

1 **Look at the photos and complete the crossword.**

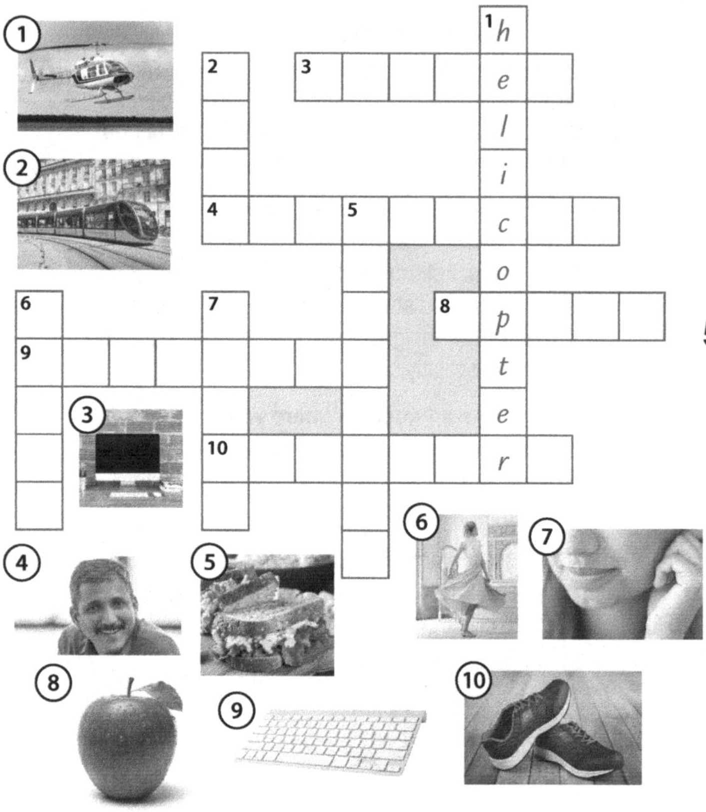

2 **Write the opposite of the adjectives.**

1 interested	2 expensive
3 fair	4 quiet
5 beautiful	6 curly
7 ill	8 heavy

bored ______________________________

____

3 **Write the words in the box in the categories.**

April aunt baker's ceiling chemist's cousin ~~dance~~ Dutch February floor Japanese May nephew play run supermarket Turkish wall

Ability verbs	*dance*
Nationality adjective	
Family	
Shops	
Parts of a room	
Months	

4 **Write the verb that goes with the words and phrases.**

1 *play* the piano, a game
2 ______ to music, to the teacher
3 ______ TV, a film
4 ______ a bag, an umbrella
5 ______ up, off a bus
6 ______ home, by train
7 ______ lunch, lessons

5 **Complete the crossword and find the secret word.**

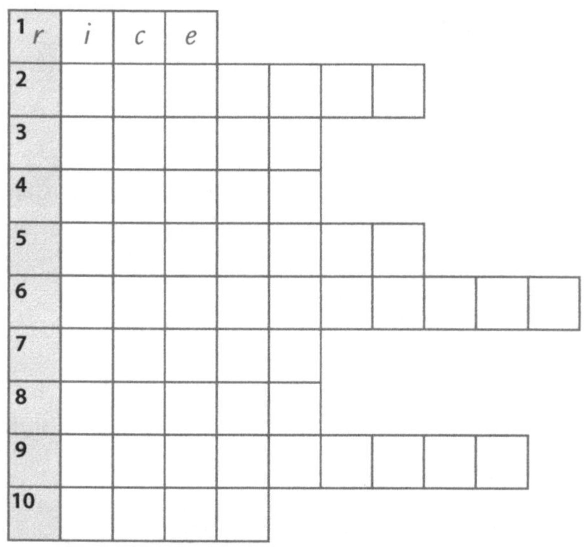

1 This food is popular in China and Japan.
2 The ordinal number of 11.
3 This is in the bathroom. It's quicker than a bath.
4 This is a small computer. It hasn't usually got a keyboard.
5 Nationality of people from the United States.
6 The metro in London.
7 If your bike has a problem you ______ it.
8 The eighth month of the year.
9 You buy newspapers and magazines in this shop.
10 These are in your mouth. They help you to eat your food.

1 There is one word missing in each sentence. Write the missing word.

1 My father's *a* waiter.
2 There three cinemas in my town.
3 You like computer games?
4 How many languages can speak?
5 There any boys in the team?
6 Where your grandparents live?
7 We can't come now. We watching a film.

2 Complete the conversation with the comparative or superlative form of the adjectives in brackets, or the possessive pronoun of the noun phrases.

Jude: Thanks for letting me use your laptop today.
Finn: No problem. Was it OK?
Jude: It's great! It's **1** *newer* **(new)** than **2** *ours* **(our laptop)** and a lot **3** ______ **(good)**!
Finn: Why?
Jude: Well **4** ______ **(your laptop)** is **5** ______ **(modern)** and it's a lot **6** ______ **(light)**.
Finn: Yes, I think it's the **7** ______ **(light)** you can buy.
Judy: Also, the keyboard on **8** ______ **(my laptop)** is very noisy. **9** ______ **(Your laptop)** is a lot **10** ______ **(quiet)**.
Finn: That's interesting.
Judy: But the **11** ______ **(good)** thing is that it's so fast. Mine is a lot **12** ______ **(slow)**. Thanks a lot.

3 Correct the sentences.

1 My mother doesn't got a car.
My mother hasn't got a car.
2 **A:** Do you like vegetables? **B:** Yes, I like.
______
3 I haven't got some homework tonight.
______
4 My cousin's names are Rebecca and Gabriel.
______
5 Is Jan's father a teacher? Yes, he's.
______
6 I can hear Mario but I can't see he.
______
7 I'm going to school every day by bus.
______

4 Match rules a–g with the sentences in exercise 3.

a Make present simple short answers with *do*/*does*. ___
b Use the present simple for repeated actions and present continuous for actions happening now. ___
c With *have got* we don't use *do* in negative sentences. *1*
d We normally use *'s* with singular nouns and *s'* with plural nouns. ___
e For the object of the sentence, use *me, you, him, her, us, them*. ___
f We normally use *some* in the affirmative and *any* in questions and negatives. ___
g Don't use a contraction in affirmative short answers. ___

5 Complete the email with the correct form of the verbs in brackets.

Hi Grandpa,

How are you? Mum **1** *said* **(say +)** you're back from Portugal. **2** ______ **(have / you)** a good holiday? **3** ______ **(be)** the hotel OK?

Last Saturday, we **4** ______ **(go +)** to see this very interesting competition. It's called *Man versus Horse*.

The competition **5** ______ **(start +)** in 1980 when Gordon Green **6** ______ **(hear +)** a conversation between two men. One man said he **7** ______ **(think +)** a person could be quicker than a horse. The other man **8** ______ **(agree –)**, so Green **9** ______ **(decide +)** to try it! He **10** ______ **(organise +)** a 35 km race. The first year the prize **11** ______ **(be +)** £1,000, but there **12** ______ **(be –)** a winner – well the winner was a horse and it **13** ______ **(get –)** the money! Every year the prize **14** ______ **(get +)** bigger, and in 2004, Huw Lobb was the first person to win the race and he **15** ______ **(win +)** £25,000!

I'm sending a photo of this year's race. It was really exciting and we **16** ______ **(have +)** a great day!

Love,
Bella

Ⓐ

REVIEWS

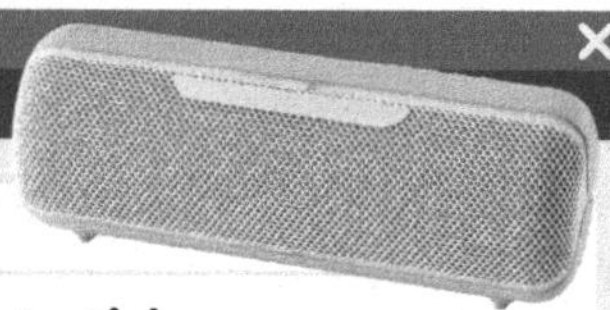

Lee, Bradford

★★★★★ **Fantastic!**

There are so many good things about this speaker: it's smaller and lighter than my old speaker, so it's very easy to carry in my bag. The sound is great: the speaker is small, but my music sounds fantastic. But for me, the best thing is the price. It only costs $19!

Esme, Denver

★★★★★ **My best birthday present!**

My aunt gave me this speaker for my birthday and when I first opened it, I wasn't happy. It was very small. But when I listened to it, I changed my opinion! It sounds fantastic. And mine is pink – I love the colour!

Gemma, Calgary

★★ **Next time, buy something better**

I agree that this speaker is cheap and the sound is OK, but the radio isn't good. I also had problems with the Bluetooth. It didn't work well with my computer.

Ⓑ

WHICH IS THE BEST COLOUR FOR YOUR ROOM?

Most students do homework and study in their bedroom, so it's important that this is the best possible place to work well. Think about some key questions. Can you see well? Is there good light from a window? Have you got a chair and a table with space to work? These are good things to think about, but there's another important question: what colour is the room?

A lot of people think that white or green is a good colour, but a new study disagrees. They say these colours are too relaxing. In a recent test, university students had to read a text and answer questions. They did the tests in rooms with six different colours: strong red, blue and yellow, and pale red, blue and yellow. The test results were much better in the strong red and yellow rooms.

So, if you want to pass your exams – ask your parents to paint your room red or yellow!

1 Match 1–4 with a–d to make reading tips.

1 Pictures can help you understand a text, *b*
2 Look at the text before you read. ___
3 Try to get a general idea the first time you read. ___
4 First, read quickly to find the part of the text with the answer. ___

a Don't stop if there's a word you don't know.
b so look at them before you read.
c Then read slowly and intensively to answer the question.
d Decide what type of information is in the text.

2 (Tips 1 and 2) Look at the texts and their photos, but don't read. Which text … ?

1 comes from a magazine about science *B*
2 comes from a shopping website ___
3 gives people's opinions ___
4 gives information from a scientific study ___
5 talks about how people study best ___
6 talks about technology ___
7 is for students ___
8 is for shoppers ___

3 (Tip 3) Read the texts quickly to check your answers in exercise 2.

4 🔊27 **(Tip 4) Read and listen to the texts and answer the questions. The questions are not in the same order as the information in the text.**

1 Who bought Esme's speaker?
Her aunt.
2 In which room do a lot of students study?
___
3 Who wasn't happy with their present at the start?
___
4 Why are windows important?
___
5 How many different colours were in the test?
___
6 How many people think the speaker is cheap?
___
7 Why does Lee like the speaker?
___
8 What's the problem with white and green?
___

1 **Match 1–4 with a–d to make listening tips.**

1 Look at photos and use them
2 When listening, it's not important
3 To choose the best summary,
4 Listen carefully so

a read the options before you listen.
b to get information before you listen.
c you know when the information is coming.
d to understand every word.

2 **(Tip 1) Match the words in the box with photos A–D.**

announcement game I haven't got time ~~It's your turn~~ questions queue station traffic

A *It's your turn* ____________

B ____________ ____________

C ____________ ____________

D ____________ ____________

3 🔊28 **(Tip 2) Listen and match recordings 1–4 to photos A–D.**

1 ___ 2 ___ 3 ___ 4 ___

4 **(Tip 3) Listen again and choose the best summary for each recording.**

1 (a) The train is 15 minutes late.
  b The train is on time.
2 a Jamie wins the game.
  b Jamie doesn't win the game.
3 a It isn't difficult for the man to do his job.
  b The man has a problem doing his job.
4 a The weather this morning is very bad.
  b The traffic this morning is very bad.

5 🔊29 **(Tip 4) Listen to recording 4 and complete the sentences with words you hear.**

1 The information is coming from *our traffic team*.
2 There's a big problem on ____________.
3 There is a queue of about ____________.
4 The reason for the problem is ____________.
5 If you can travel by a different road, that's ____________.

Speaking

1 Complete the table with the phrases in the box.

~~Are you free on (day)?~~ I'm from …
Is (time) OK? Nice to meet you.
Sorry, I'm busy Sunday's good.
What's your name? Where are you from?
Why don't we (verb)? Yes, great.

Meeting new people	
Making suggestions	*Are you free on (day)?*
Saying *Yes/No* to suggestions	

2 Complete the conversation with phrases from the table.

Leo: Hi. Is this your first day at the Photography Club?

Felix: Yes, it is. I'm Felix. 1 *What's your name?*

Leo: I'm Leo. **2** ____________________, Felix.

Felix: Nice to meet you, too. **3** ____________________?

Leo: I'm from Watford, but now we live in Kenton.

Felix: I live there, too! **4** ____________________ meet on Saturday to take some photos?

Leo: Sorry, **5** ____________________ on Saturday. **6** ____________________ on Sunday?

Felix: Yes, Sunday's good. Is 11:00 at the station OK?

Leo: **7** ____________________. See you then.

Felix: See you. Bye.

3 Keira is asking a tourist information officer about visiting Wembley Stadium in London. Who says each phrase? Write K (Keira) or O (Tourist Information Officer).

a Can I help you? *O*
b OK, and finally, how much does it cost? ___
c It costs £17. Buy your ticket online – it's cheaper. ___
d It's open every day from 10:00 am to 5:00 pm. ___
e Of course – what do you want to know? ___
f OK, ten o'clock to five o'clock. And how can I get there? ___
g OK, great. Thank you. ___
h The underground. Take the Circle line to Wembley Park. ___
i Well first, what time does it open? ___
j What's the fastest way? ___
k Yes, I'd like some information about visiting Wembley Stadium. ___
l You can go by bus or underground. ___

4 Order the conversation in exercise 3.

1	*a*	**7**	___
2	___	**8**	___
3	___	**9**	___
4	___	**10**	___
5	___	**11**	___
6	___	**12**	___

1 Add the missing capital letters and apostrophes to this keypal message.

(1) Hi Manuel – how are you? I hope you had a good time on holiday.

(2) In your message, you asked me to tell you about my best friend and about his hobbies.

(3) M ~~my~~ best friend, C ~~charlie~~, isnt english; he's half canadian and half german. His mums family is from toronto and charlie normally spends the summer at his grandparents house. charlies father is from berlin.

(4) charlies got a sister, karin. Shes 14. karin and i are in the same music group. charlies parents work at the weekend, so karin and charlie sometimes spend saturday and sunday with their grandparents.

2 Match a–d to paragraphs 1–4.

a Talking about Charlie's nationality and family. ___
b Saying hello. ___
c More information about Charlie's family. ___
d Introducing the subject of the email. ___

3 Continue the message with another paragraph. Invent information about Charlie's hobbies.

____
____
____
____
____

4 Complete the blog posts with the words in the box.

after also and ~~because~~ before but so

WHAT'S THE SAME? WHAT'S DIFFERENT?

Each week, we ask readers around the world to tell us about their lives. This week's question is 'What time do you get up at the weekend?'

Jamie, Cape Town

On Saturdays, I get up late **1** *because* I get up at 6:30 am on school days. **2** ________ I get up, I have a big breakfast **3** ________ then I go shopping. I **4** ________ get up late on Sundays – I love my bed! ♡

Meena, Delhi

I don't like getting up early at the weekend, **5** ________ I have hockey training at 8:30 am on Saturdays. ☹ On Sundays, I don't get up until 12:00 pm!

Patrice, Lyon

For me Saturday is a school day, **6** ________ I get up at 7:00 am. ☹ **7** ________ school, I have breakfast with my parents. On Sundays, we all get up late. It's my favourite day!

5 Answer the question in the blog for you.

____
____
____

6 Choose one task and write your answer.

A Write a keypal message with information about your best friend.

B Invent answers for a blog post about the question 'What do you do on Sunday evenings?'

7 Answer the questions.

Do you use logical paragraphs? ☐
Do you use capital letters correctly? ☐
Do you use apostrophes for possession and for contractions? ☐
Do you connect your ideas with *and, but, because, so, also, before* and *after*? ☐

Irregular verbs

Infinitive	Past simple	Past participle	Translation
be /biː/	**was/were** /wɒz/ /wɜː(r)/	**been** /biːn/	
become /bɪ'kʌm/	**became** /bɪ'keɪm/	**become** /bɪ'kʌm/	
break /breɪk/	**broke** /brəʊk/	**broken** /'brəʊkən/	
bring /brɪŋ/	**brought** /brɔːt/	**brought** /brɔːt/	
buy /baɪ/	**bought** /bɔːt/	**bought** /bɔːt/	
choose /tʃuːz/	**chose** /tʃəʊz/	**chosen** /'tʃəʊz(ə)n/	
come /kʌm/	**came** /keɪm/	**come** /kʌm/	
do /duː/	**did** /dɪd/	**done** /dʌn/	
drink /drɪŋk/	**drank** /dræŋk/	**drunk** /drʌŋk/	
eat /iːt/	**ate** /eɪt/	**eaten** /'iːt(ə)n/	
fall /fɔːl/	**fell** /fel/	**fallen** /'fɔːlən/	
feel /fiːl/	**felt** /felt/	**felt** /felt/	
find /faɪnd/	**found** /faʊnd/	**found** /faʊnd/	
forget /fə(r)'get/	**forgot** /fə(r)'gɒt/	**forgotten** /fə(r)'gɒt(ə)n/	
get /get/	**got** /gɒt/	**got** /gɒt/	
give /gɪv/	**gave** /geɪv/	**given** /'gɪv(ə)n/	
go /gəʊ/	**went** /went/	**gone** /gɒn/	
have /hæv/	**had** /hæd/	**had** /hæd/	
know /nəʊ/	**knew** /njuː/	**known** /nəʊn/	
leave /liːv/	**left** /left/	**left** /left/	
lose /luːz/	**lost** /lɒst/	**lost** /lɒst/	
make /meɪk/	**made** /meɪd/	**made** /meɪd/	
meet /miːt/	**met** /met/	**met** /met/	
put /pʊt/	**put** /pʊt/	**put** /pʊt/	
read /riːd/	**read** /red/	**read** /red/	
ride /raɪd/	**rode** /rəʊd/	**ridden** /'rɪd(ə)n/	
run /rʌn/	**ran** /ræn/	**run** /rʌn/	
say /seɪ/	**said** /sed/	**said** /sed/	
see /siː/	**saw** /sɔː/	**seen** /siːn/	
send /send/	**sent** /sent/	**sent** /sent/	
sleep /sliːp/	**slept** /slept/	**slept** /slept/	
speak /spiːk/	**spoke** /spəʊk/	**spoken** /'spəʊkən/	
spend /spend/	**spent** /spent/	**spent** /spent/	
take /teɪk/	**took** /tʊk/	**taken** /'teɪkən/	
tell /tel/	**told** /təʊld/	**told** /təʊld/	
think /θɪŋk/	**thought** /θɔːt/	**thought** /θɔːt/	
understand /ˌʌndə(r)'stænd/	**understood** /ˌʌndə(r)'stʊd/	**understood** /ˌʌndə(r)'stʊd/	
wake /weɪk/	**woke** /wəʊk/	**woken** /'wəʊkən/	
win /wɪn/	**won** /wʌn/	**won** /wʌn/	
write /raɪt/	**wrote** /rəʊt/	**written** /'rɪt(ə)n/	

Contents

Competence builder

Subject pronouns and possessive adjectives

Subject pronoun	Possessive adjective
I	my
you	your
he	his
she	her
it	its
we	our
they	their

- we use *I*, *you*, *he*, *she*, *it*, *we* and *they* to describe the subject of the sentence
  We *are in year seven.*
  He *is a teacher.*
- we always write the pronoun *I* with a capital letter
  Jess is from England and ***I****'m from Spain.*
- we use *my*, *your*, *his*, *her*, *its*, *our* and *their* before a noun to show possession
  It's ***my*** *bag.*
  This is ***our*** *classroom.*

a, *an* and plurals

- we use the article *a* before singular nouns starting with a consonant sound
  a *computer,* ***a*** *hotel*
- we use the article *an* before singular nouns starting with a vowel sound
  an *umbrella,* ***an*** *email address*
- we form the plural for most nouns by adding *-s*
  school → *school****s***
  key → *key****s***
- for nouns that end *-ch*, *-sh*, *-s*, *-ss* and *-x*, add *-es*
  address → *address****es***
  box → *box****es***
- for nouns that end in consonant + *-y*, omit the *-y* and add *-ies*
  baby → *bab****ies***
  story → *stor****ies***

this, that, these, those

	Near	At a distance
Singular	this	that
Plural	these	those

- we use *this* for singular nouns that are near
  This *is my friend, Jan.*
- we use *that* for singular nouns that are at a distance
  That*'s my mum in the car park.*
- we use *these* for plural nouns that are near
  Are ***these*** *your keys?*
- we use *those* for plural nouns that are at a distance
  Those *boys over there are in our class.*

Imperatives

- we use imperatives to give instructions
- the positive form is the same as the infinitive
  Open *your books.*
  Do *the exercise.*
- we make the negative imperative with *don't* + infinitive
  Don't *write in your books.*
  Please ***don't*** *talk.*

Subject pronouns and possessive adjectives

1 Order the words to make sentences. Then choose the correct word in brackets.

1 isn't / phone / This / **(my/I)**
This isn't my phone.
2 **(you/your)** / are / How ?
______
3 Mr Scott / teacher's / **(We/Our)** / is / name
______
4 brother / school / Is / in this / **(you/your)** ?
______
5 for English / **(We/Our)** / in this / aren't / classroom
______
6 Spanish / Jack's Dutch / **(his/she)** / is / but / mum
______

a, an and plurals

2 Complete the dialogue with *a* or *an*.

A: Excuse me, have you got my bag?
B: What colour is it?
A: It's **1** *a* black bag with white letters on it.
B: I've got two black bags here. What's in your bag?
A: Let me think – **2** ______ orange notebook, **3** ______ pencil case, **4** ______ English book, **5** ______ apple and **6** ______ mobile phone.

3 Complete the table.

Singular	Plural
window	1 *windows*
2 ______	doctors
computer	3 ______
4 ______	cinemas
5 ______	boxes
address	6 ______
7 ______	watches
sandwich	8 ______
party	9 ______
10 ______	babies
11 ______	cities
family	12 ______

this, that, these, those

4 Change the sentences as indicated: *singular* to *plural*, *near* to *at a distance*. Remember to change the verb if necessary.

1 This is my book. **(plural)**
These are my books.
2 Those are my apples. **(near)**
______
3 Is that your dad's car? **(near)**
______
4 These are my pencils. **(singular)**
______
5 This is my sister, Beth. **(at a distance)**
______
6 This is my bag. **(plural)**
______
7 Are these your notebooks? **(at a distance)**
______
8 That's my friend. **(plural)**
______

Imperatives

5 Which instructions are correct? There are three.

1 Don't not talk in the library.
2 Check your answers in pairs.
3 Please to write your answers in pencil.
4 Don't copying the vocabulary.
5 Open the window, Carlos.
6 Don't eat in the classroom.
7 Listen the conversation and write the answers.
8 Working in groups of three.

be: affirmative

Full form		Contracted form	
I am	a teacher.	I'm	Mexican.
You are We are They are	Spanish.	You're We're They're	from Paris.
He is She is It is	from China.	He's She's It's	Dutch.

- the verb *be* has two forms: full and contracted; we normally use contracted forms after pronouns
- to make a contraction, we omit a letter from the verb and mark the missing letter with an apostrophe (')
- we use *am* after *I*; for the contracted form, we omit *a-*
  ~~*am*~~ → ***'m***
  *I'**m** 11. Yes, I **am** Mexican.*
- we use *are* after *you* (singular and plural), *we* and *they*; for the contracted form, we omit *a-*
  ~~*are*~~ → ***'re***
  *You'**re** in this class. Jose and Miguel **are** from Seville. They'**re** in the city centre.*
- we use *is* after *he*, *she* and *it*; for the contracted form we omit *i-*
  ~~*is*~~ → ***'s***
  *He'**s** from Poland. Our teacher **is** in a meeting. The cat **is** very old.*

be: negative

- we form the negative of the verb *be* with *not* after the verb
  *I'm **not** in this class.*
  *He is**n't** eleven.*
  *We are**n't** in Class 8A.*
- notice the contracted form
  *I am → I'**m** not*
  *You are → You are**n't** (Also possible: you'**re** not)*
  *We are → We are**n't** (We'**re** not)*
  *They are → They are**n't** (They'**re** not)*
  *He is → He is**n't** (He'**s** not)*
  *She is → She is**n't** (She'**s** not)*
  *It is → It is**n't** (It'**s** not)*

be: questions and short answers

- to make questions with *be*, we put the verb before the subject
  ***Are** you Japanese?* ***Is** this your bag?*
- there are no contractions in the question form
- we don't use contractions in affirmative short answers, but we use contractions in negative short answers
  *Are they in your class? Yes, **they are**. ~~Yes, they're.~~*
  *Is he in the football team? No, **he isn't**.*

Question	Affirmative short answer	Negative short answer
Am I in this class?	Yes, I am.	No, I'm not.
Are you/we/they from Australia?	Yes, you/we/they are.	No, you/we/they aren't.
Is he/she/it Chinese?	Yes, he/she/it is.	No, he/she/it isn't.

be: affirmative

1 Match 1–6 with a–f to make sentences.

1 Carole's mother — c
2 My friend and I
3 I
4 Dubai
5 They
6 He

a is a very modern city.
b 're teachers.
c is from Canada.
d 's 12.
e are in the same class.
f 'm in the basketball team.

2 Complete the sentences with the affirmative form of *be*. Use contracted forms if possible.

1 This city *is* very old.
2 Those dogs ______ very ugly.
3 My brother and I ______ in a band.
4 You ______ in Class 7C.
5 She ______ my English teacher.
6 My friend Altan ______ 12.

be: negative

3 Rewrite the sentences in the negative form.

1 This is my bag.
This isn't my bag.
2 Micky and James are brothers.
______
3 I'm Spanish.
______
4 You're in this class.
______
5 She's our sports teacher.
______
6 Singapore is a dirty city.
______

4 Correct the sentences with the information in brackets.

1 Athens is a modern city. **(old)**
Athens isn't a modern city. It's an old city.
2 My sister and I are from Lisbon. **(Porto)**
______
3 Alaska and Siberia are hot places. **(cold)**
______
4 Machu Picchu is in Brazil. **(Peru)**
______
5 I'm from Birmingham. **(Manchester)**
______

be: questions and short answers

5 Which question is correct, a or b?

1 (a) Are you from Argentina?
b You are from Argentina?
2 a Are she Martin's sister?
b Is she Martin's sister?
3 a Is your Dad a doctor?
b Are your Dad a doctor?
4 a Are your parents at home?
b Are at home your parents?
5 a Am I in your group.
b Am I in your group?

6 Match questions 1–6 with answers a–f.

1 Is your name Lara? *b*
2 Are you 12?
3 Are your parents from Chile?
4 Is your sister married?
5 Are we good at English?
6 Is Daniel your brother?

a Yes, she is.
b No, it isn't.
c Yes, he is.
d Yes, we are.
e No, they aren't.
f No, I'm not.

7 Write complete questions and answers.

1 Detroit / a noisy / city ? **(+)**
Is Detroit a noisy city?
Yes, it is.
2 Morocco / in Europe ? **(–)**
______
______
3 your mother / Australian ? **(+)**
______
______
4 Istanbul and Rio de Janeiro / capital cities ? **(–)**
______
______
5 your parents / from the same country ? **(+)**
______
______

have got: affirmative and negative

Affirmative	
I/You/We/They	've got (have got) a car.
He/She/It	's got (has got) a pet.

Negative	
I/You/We/They	haven't got (have not got) a computer.
He/She/It	hasn't got (has not got) any cousins.

Affirmative	Negative
I've got a car.	I haven't got a computer.
You've got a car.	You haven't got a computer.
He's got a car.	He hasn't got a computer.
She's got a car.	She hasn't got a computer.
It's got a car.	It hasn't got a computer.
We've got a car.	We haven't got a computer.
They've got a car.	They haven't got a computer.

- we use *have got* to talk about possession
- *have got* has two forms: full and contracted; we normally use contracted forms after pronouns
  *I**'ve got** two brothers.*
  *Jane and Freddy **have got** a house in France.*
- we use *have got* after *I*, *you* (singular and plural), *we* and *they*; for the affirmative contracted form, we omit *ha-*
  have got → ***'ve got***
  *We**'ve got** Mrs Clark for English this year.*
- for the negative contracted form, we omit the *-o-* in *not*
  have not got → ***haven't got***
  *I **haven't got** brown hair.*
- we use *has got* after *he*, *she* and *it*; for the affirmative contracted form, we omit *ha-*
  has got → ***'s got***
  *She**'s got** green eyes.*
- for the negative contracted form, we omit the *-o-* in *not*
  has not got → ***hasn't got***
  *He **hasn't got** a pen.*

Possessive *'s*

- we use an apostrophe (') to show possession
- we use *'s* with a singular noun
  *my sister**'s** husband*
- we normally write an apostrophe (without *-s*) after a plural noun
  *This is my grandparents**'** house.*
- with irregular plurals which don't end in *-s*, we add *'s* for possession
  *the children**'s** mother*

have got: questions and short answers

Questions		Short answers		
Have I/you/we/they	got a sister?	Yes,	I / you / we / they	have.
		No,		haven't.
Has he/she/it		Yes,	he / she / it	has.
		No,		hasn't.

- to make questions with *have got*, we put the subject between *have*/*has* and *got*
  ***Have we got** English class today?*
  ***Has she got** any hobbies?*
- we don't use contractions in affirmative short answers, but we use contractions in negative short answers
  Have you got a cat? *Yes, **I have**.*
  Has it got a name? *No, **it hasn't**.*

have got: affirmative and negative

1 Match a–b with 1–2 to make sentences.

1 a Sarah — 2 's got blue eyes.
  b I haven't — 1 got a black pen.
2 a Our car — 1 hasn't got a radio.
  b My friends — 2 haven't got any money.
3 a We have — 1 has got a moustache.
  b Our teacher — 2 n't got English today.

2 Write complete sentences with *have got*.

1 Julia / a sister
Julia's got a sister.
2 We / a big car
___
3 The teacher / not / a key to the classroom
___
4 I / not / a bicycle
___
5 My city / not / an airport
___

Possessive *'s*

3 Choose the correct answer.

1 *Laura's* mother is a doctor.
a Lauras b Laura's c Lauras'
2 My ___ phone isn't blue; it's black.
a fathers b fathers' c father's
3 My ___ are in a different class.
a friends b friend's c friends'
4 Is that your ___ car?
a teacher b teachers c teacher's

4 Are the sentences correct or incorrect? Correct the incorrect sentences.

1 George is Melanie son.
George is Melanie's son.
2 That's my mothers' umbrella.
___
3 This is my sister's house.
___
4 It's Silvias party tonight!
___
5 My cousin's names are Archie and Bethany.
___

have got: questions and short answers

5 Complete the questions with the missing words.

1 *Have* I got a piano lesson this evening?
2 Have we ___ football on Saturday?
3 ___ your brother got a lot of homework?
4 ___ your friends got a party this weekend?
5 ___ you got time to meet today?
6 Has the class ___ an exam this week?

6 Match short answers a–f with the questions in exercise 5.

a No, he hasn't. ___
b Yes, you have. *1*
c Yes, it has. ___
d No, I'm sorry, I haven't. ___
e No, we haven't. ___
f Yes, they have. ___

7 Correct the mistakes.

1 **A:** Has your school got a computer centre?
B: No, ~~it haven't~~.
No, it hasn't.
2 **A:** Has your grandmother got glasses?
B: Yes, have.
___
3 **A:** Have your grandfather got a beard?
B: No, he hasn't.
___
4 **A:** Have your parents got two cars?
B: Yes, they've.
___
5 **A:** Has your sister and brother got any hobbies?
B: Yes, they have.
___
6 **A:** Have you got any books about robots?
B: No, we hasn't.
___

Countable and uncountable nouns

- we can count some things
- before singular countable nouns, we use *a/an* or the number *one*

  ***a** computer, **an** umbrella, **one** bag*
- before plural countable nouns, we use a number or *some*

  *I've got **two** pens and **some** books.*
- some things are uncountable; they don't have a plural
- before uncountable nouns, we use *some* or nothing

  *They've got pasta, water, **some** juice and **some** cheese.*
- some nouns are both countable (if an individual thing) and uncountable (if a part of a big thing)

  *I'd like **an** ice cream. (= an individual one, only for me)*

  *I'd like **some** ice cream. (= a portion, part of a bigger quantity)*

some, any, a lot of

- we use *some* with both countable nouns in the plural and uncountable nouns

  *We've got **some** apples and **some** bread.*
- we use *a lot of* with both countable and uncountable nouns to describe a big number or amount

  *My school has got **a lot of** students.*

  *He's got **a lot of** money.*
- we use *any* with negative sentences and questions

  *He hasn't got **any** cousins.*

  *Have you got **any** free time today?*

there is/are

	Affirmative	Negative
Singular	There's (There is) a hospital.	There isn't a cinema.
Plural	There are some students in the classroom.	There aren't any buses.

	Question	Short answers
Singular	Is there a doctor here?	Yes, there is./ No, there isn't.
Plural	Are there any taxis?	Yes, there are./ No, there aren't.

- we use *there is/there are* to describe the things in a place
- we use *there is* before singular or uncountable nouns

  ***There's** a hotel near the station.*

  ***Is there** any cheese?*
- we use *there are* before plural nouns

  ***There are** 25 students in my class.*

Countable and uncountable nouns

1 Decide if the words are countable (C) or uncountable (U).

1 coffee _U_
2 oil ___
3 sandwich ___
4 nephew ___
5 hair ___
6 taxi ___

2 Complete the sentences with *a*, *an* or *some*.

1 My sister's got ___*a*___ boyfriend.
2 Oh, no. I haven't got ______ umbrella!
3 I've got ______ emails to answer.
4 We've got ______ Australian boy in our class.
5 Naomi's got ______ water.
6 It's ______ book about insects.

some, any, a lot of

3 Write sentences with *have got* and *some*, *any* or *a lot of*.

1 water (+++)
We've got a lot of water.
2 money (+)
______
3 books (+++)
______
4 pencils (0)
______
5 homework (+)
______
6 exams (0)
______

4 Choose the correct option.

Paolo: Have you got 1 **some/any** books to take home?
Librarian: Yes, we've got 2 **any/a lot of** books you can take home.
Paolo: Have you got 3 **some/any** computers to use here?
Librarian: Yes, we've got 4 **any/some** computers in the student study area.
Paolo: Have you got 5 **any/a lot of** books about karate?
Librarian: We haven't got 6 **any/some** books only about karate, but we've got 7 **some/any** books about sport.

there is/are

5 Complete the sentences with *is* or *are*.

1 There ___*are*___ three computers.
2 There ______ a restaurant.
3 There ______ some cafés.
4 There ______ some bread.
5 There ______ an umbrella.
6 There ______ a lot of potatoes.

6 Complete the sentences with *is*, *isn't*, *are* or *aren't*. Use contractions where possible.

There **1** ___*are*___ a lot of students from other countries in my class. There **2** ______ two boys from Romania and there **3** ______ a girl from Panama. There **4** ______ four students from China. There **5** ______ some students from South America, but there **6** ______ any people from the USA. There **7** ______ a problem with language. Everyone speaks English.

Present simple: affirmative

- we use the present simple to talk about routine actions and facts
- for *I*, *you*, *we* and *they*, the form is the same as the infinitive

  *I **live** in Monterrey.* *They **get up** at 7:00.*
- for *he*, *she* and *it*, we add *-s* to most verbs

  *She live**s** in Monterrey.* *He get**s** up at 8:00.*

Spelling: present simple third person singular

- most verbs add *-s*

  *start → it start**s***
- for verbs that end in *-o*, *-ch*, *-sh* and *-x*, add *-es*

  *go → he go**es***

  *watch → she watch**es***
- for verbs that end in consonant + *-y*, change to *-ies*

  *study → he stud**ies***
- some verbs are irregular

  *have → she **has***

Present simple: negative

- after *I*, *you*, *we*, and *they*, we form the negative with *don't* + verb

  *I **don't speak** German.* *They **don't go** to my school.*
- after *he*, *she* and *it*, we form the negative with *doesn't* + verb

  *She **doesn't have** lunch at school.*

  *That cat **doesn't eat** fish.*

Present simple: *Yes/No* questions and short answers

- we use *do* to make *Yes/No* questions and short answers with *I*, *you*, *we*, *they*

  ***Do** you live here?* *Yes, I **do**./No, I **don't**.*
- we use *does* to make *Yes/No* questions and short answers with *he*, *she*, *it*

  ***Does** your friend play the guitar?*

  *Yes, he **does**./No, he **doesn't**.*

Present simple: *Wh-* questions

- we use a question word (*Who*, *What*, etc.) and *do* to make *Wh-* questions with *I*, *you*, *we*, *they*

  ***What** time **do** classes start?*
- we use a question word (*Who*, *What*, etc.) and *does* to make *Wh-* questions with *he*, *she*, *it*

  ***Where does** your mother work?*

love/like/don't like/hate + noun

Subject	Object
I	me
you	you
he	him
she	her
it	it
we	us
they	them

- we use pronouns with *like*, *love*, *hate*, etc. to describe the object of an action

  ***I love** it!* ***She hates** them.*

Present simple: affirmative

1 Write the third person singular of the verbs.

1 write *writes*
2 read ________
3 finish ________
4 have ________
5 play ________
6 copy ________
7 do ________
8 drink ________

2 Complete the sentences with the correct form of the verbs in brackets.

1 Jan *plays* the guitar. **(play)**
2 Misha and Sebastian ________ judo. **(do)**
3 Clare ________ Chinese. **(study)**
4 My grandmother ________ in Warsaw. **(live)**
5 The people in my class ________ video games. **(love)**
6 My best friend ________ at my house on Fridays. **(stay)**

Present simple: negative

3 Write complete negative sentences.

1 I / play / the piano
I don't play the piano.
2 Shari / listen / to the teacher
____
3 My cousins / live / in Texas
____
4 We / speak / French
____

4 Complete the text with the correct form of the verbs in brackets.

3.75 million people **1** *visit* **(visit / +)** the London Eye every year. The Eye is a very big wheel. It **2** ________ **(move / +)** very slowly and it **3** ________ **(stop / –)** all day. On the Eye, visitors **4** ________ **(take / +)** photos and they **5** ________ **(enjoy / +)** the fantastic views of London. The Eye **6** ________ **(open / –)** at the same time all year: the opening hours **7** ________ **(change / +)**. This week, it **8** ________ **(open / +)** at 11:00 and **9** ________ **(close / +)** at 18:00. It **10** ________ **(close / –)** at lunchtime. Ticket prices **11** ________ **(start / +)** from £27.

Present simple: *Yes/No* questions and short answers

5 Complete the dialogues with *do, does, don't, doesn't, like* or *likes*.

1 **Ian:** *Do* you *like* Indian food?
Ben: No, I ________ .
2 **Jay:** ________ your friend ________ basketball?
Kim: No, he ________ . He ________ tennis.

Present simple: *Wh-* questions

6 Write questions about the underlined information.

1 I live in Liverpool.
Where do you live?
2 She gets up at half past seven.
____
3 He has fruit for breakfast.
____
4 Their grandmother cooks their dinner.
____
5 We go shopping at the supermarket.
____

love/like/don't like/hate + noun

7 Choose the correct option.

1 Your parents are very nice – I like **him/them**.
2 My piano teacher is very strict; he's a good teacher, but I don't like **he/him**.
3 This book is great – I love **it/her**.
4 Tania is great – all the class like **her/she**.
5 We don't like our music teacher and she doesn't like **we/us**.
6 I like Freddy, but I don't think he likes **her/me**.

can and *can't*

I/You/He/She/It/We/They	can swim. can't swim.

- we use *can* to talk about ability
- after *can* we use the infinitive without *to*
  *I **can** dance the tango.*
- we don't add *-s* in the third person singular
  *Stephen **can** play the guitar.*
- we don't use the auxiliary *do* with *can* in the negative form
- we use *not* (contraction *n't*) to form the negative
  *They **can't** speak French.* *I **can't** cook.*

can: questions and short answers

Questions			Short answers
	Can you play	the piano?	Yes, I can. No, I can't.
Which languages	can you speak?		French and Spanish.

- to make a *Yes/No* question, we put the verb before the subject
- to make a short answer, we use *Yes, (I) can./No, (I) can't.*
  ***Can** she ride a bike?* *No, she **can't**.*
- to make a *Wh-* question, we use a question word (*Who*, *What*, etc.) before *can*
  ***What can** you cook?*

Comparative adjectives

- we use a comparative adjective to compare two things
- after the comparative adjective, we use *than*
  *Jack is taller **than** Sam.*

Spelling: comparative adjectives

One-syllable adjectives	
add *-er*	tall – taller short – shorter
Most one-syllable adjectives ending in consonant + vowel + consonant	
double final consonant and add *-er*	hot – hotter thin – thinner
Two-syllable adjectives ending in *-y*	
change to *-ier*	heavy – heavier curly – curlier
Adjectives with two or more syllables	
use *more* + adjective	boring – more boring dangerous – more dangerous
Irregular adjectives	
	good – better bad – worse

Possessive pronouns

- we use a possessive adjective before a noun
  *That's **my** bag.*
- we use a possessive pronoun when there is no noun
  *It's **mine**.*

Subject pronoun	Possessive adjective	Possessive pronoun
I	my	mine
you	your	yours
he	his	his
she	her	hers
it	its	–
we	our	ours
they	their	theirs

can and *can't*

1 Choose the correct option.

1 **A:** Can you **play/to play** the guitar?
B: No, I **can/can't**.
2 We **can't/don't can** speak Spanish.
3 Jamie **cans/can** carry your bag.
4 **A: You can help me/Can you help me** with the homework?
B: Yes, can/Yes, I can.

can: questions and short answers

2 Write complete conversations.

1 he / run fast ? **(+)**
Can he run fast?
Yes, he can.
2 you / spell *keyboard*? **(+)**
______
______
3 your grandfather / use a touchpad? **(–)**
______
______
4 your friends / play any musical instruments? **(–)**
______
______
5 you / cook dinner tonight? **(+)**
______
______
6 Elena / sing **(–)**
______
______

Comparative adjectives

3 Write the comparative of the adjectives.

1 tall *taller*
2 cold ______
3 beautiful ______
4 bad ______
5 heavy ______
6 old ______
7 thin ______
8 slow ______

4 Write comparative sentences about the information with the adjectives in the box.

cheap/expensive	fast/slow	old/young	~~short/tall~~

1 Ray is 1 m 65.
Jon is 1 m 78.
Ray is shorter than Jon. Jon is taller than Ray.
2 The XJ Reflex Camera costs €290.
The Snappit Camera costs €99.
______
3 Going to school by car takes 15 minutes.
Going to school by bus takes 35 minutes.
______
4 My sister is ten years old.
My brother is eight years old.
______

Possessive pronouns

5 Which sentence is correct?

1 Those books are my. ✗
2 Where's Tom? Is that bike him?
3 Are these pens your?
4 That laptop is hers.
5 This is our table and that one is theres.

6 Correct the incorrect sentences in exercise 5.

1 Those books are mine.
______
______
______

7 Complete the sentences with the correct possessive pronoun.

Conversation 1
A: Is that Harry's mobile?
B: No, it isn't, it's **1 (my mobile)** *mine*. Harry's is black and **2 (my mobile)** ______ is blue.

Conversation 2
A: Is this book **3 (your book)** ______?
B: No, it's not **4 (my book)** ______. Ask Roberta. I think it's **5 (her book)** ______.

Conversation 3
A: Which table is **6 (your table)** ______?
B: The one next to the door.
A: No, Karen says that's **7 (their table)** ______.
B: Yes, **8 (her table)** ______ is on the left. **9 (Our table)** ______ is on the right.

Present continuous: affirmative and negative

Affirmative	Negative
I'm listening to music.	I'm not listening to music.
You/We/They're listening to music.	You/We/They aren't listening to music.
He/She/It's listening to music.	He/She/It isn't listening to music.

- we use the present continuous to talk about actions happening now
- we make the present continuous with the affirmative or negative of the verb *be* and verb *-ing*
- we use time expressions like *today*, *(right) now*, *this week*, *at the moment* with the present continuous; they are usually at the end of a sentence

  *I'm **doing** my homework **now**.*

  *They **aren't watching** TV **at the moment**.*

Spelling: verb *-ing*

- most verbs add *-ing*

  eat → eating *see → seeing*
- for verbs ending in *-e*, omit the *-e* and add *-ing*

  write → writing *have → having*
- for most verbs ending in consonant + vowel + consonant, double the final consonant and add *-ing*

  chat → chatting *stop → stopping*

Present continuous: *Yes/No* questions and short answers

be	Subject	Verb *-ing*	Short answers
Am	I	dancing?	Yes, I am. No, I'm not.
Are	you we they		Yes, you/we/they are. No, you/we/they aren't.
Is	he she it		Yes, he/she/it is. No, he/she/it isn't.

- we make *Yes/No* questions by putting the verb *be* before the subject

  ***Is he** playing a video game?*

  ***Are they** watching a film?*
- we make short answers with the verb *be*
- we don't make a contraction in an affirmative short answer

  *Yes, **he is**.* *No, they aren't.*

Present continuous: *Wh-* questions

Question word	*be*	Subject	Verb *-ing*
What	am	I	reading?
	are	you we they	
	is	he she it	

- in *Wh-* questions, the order is question word + *be* + subject + verb *-ing*

  Where is she working? *Why are they running?*

Present continuous: affirmative and negative

1 Write the *-ing* form of the verbs.

1 go *going*
2 clean ______
3 read ______
4 make ______
5 chat ______
6 meet ______
7 shop ______
8 play ______
9 change ______
10 do ______

2 Write affirmative sentences using verbs from exercise 1.

1 Jane *is meeting* her friends.
2 Rory ______ the windows.
3 We ______ our homework.
4 I ______ to the shopping centre.
5 My cousins ______ a video game.
6 My mum ______ a book.

3 Order the words to make negative sentences.

1 isn't / The film / starting
The film isn't starting.
2 and Frank / swimming / Bernie / aren't
______
3 Spanish / now / speaking / The teacher / isn't
______
4 playing / We / today / aren't / tennis
______
5 aren't / with us / dinner / cousins / having / My
______

4 Complete the sentences with the verbs in the box in the affirmative or negative form.

~~cook~~ do listen stay swim

1 Ted's in the kitchen. He *'s cooking* dinner.
2 They ______ today. It's too cold.
3 Please be quiet. The students ______ an exam in here.
4 I ______ to music – it's a podcast.
5 We ______ in the Grand Hotel, not the Strand Hotel.

Present continuous: *Yes/No* questions and short answers

5 Put the words in brackets in the correct position in the question.

1 **Q:** Is anyone *sitting* here? **(sitting)**
A: No, you can take the chair.

2 **Q:** Are enjoying the party? **(you)**
A: Not much. I don't know anyone.

3 **Q:** Is your mum working? **(today)**
A: Yes, she finishes at six o'clock.

4 **Q:** Is raining? **(it)**
A: Not now, but take an umbrella.

5 **Q:** Are you OK? **(feeling)**
A: Yes, I'm fine.

6 Write the answers in exercise 5 as short answers.

1 *No, they aren't.*
2 ______
3 ______
4 ______
5 ______

Present continuous: *Wh-* questions

7 Correct the sentences.

1 Where do you going?
Where are you going?
2 What those people are doing?
______
3 What are your grandmother making for lunch?
______
4 Why are you wear sunglasses?
______
5 What are your watching?
______
6 Why everybody is running?
______

Past simple of *be*: affirmative and negative

Affirmative	Negative
I/He/She/It was ill.	I/He/She/It wasn't (was not) cold.
You/We/They were ill.	You/We/They weren't (were not) cold.

- the past simple of the verb *be* is *was/were*

  *I **was** at my uncle's house.*

  *We **were** late for class.*

- we form the negative with *not*, normally contracted to *n't*

  *Jim was**n't** at school.*

  *My parents were**n't** at home.*

- with the past simple, we use finished time expressions (e.g. *yesterday*, *last week*)

  *My mother was in London **yesterday**.*

Past simple of *be: Yes/No* questions and short answers

- to make *Yes/No* questions with *was/were*, we put the verb *be* first
- we form short answers with *was/were*
- we don't contract the verb in the affirmative short answer

  Was he an actor?

  *Yes, **he was**. / No, he wasn't.*

  Were they at the cinema?

  *Yes, **they were**. / No, they weren't.*

Past simple of *be*: *Wh-* questions

- to make *Wh-* questions, the order is question word (*Who*, *What*, etc.) + *be* + subject

  Where was the teacher?

  How much were your trousers?

Past simple of regular verbs: affirmative

- we use the past simple to talk about finished actions in the past
- to form the past simple, add *-ed* to regular verbs
- the verb is the same for all subjects (*I, you, he, she, it, we, they*)

  The class started at 9:00.

  Yesterday evening we watched a film.

Spelling: past simple of regular verbs

- most verbs add *-ed*

  *walk → walk**ed*** *finish → finish**ed***

- for verbs that end in *-e*, add *-d*

  *decide → decide**d*** *dance → dance**d***

- for verbs that end in *-y*, change to *-ied*

  *carry → carr**ied*** *study → stud**ied***

- for verbs that end in consonant + vowel + consonant, double the final consonant and add *-ed*

  *plan → pla**nned*** *stop → sto**pped***

Past simple of irregular verbs: affirmative

- some verbs are irregular in the past simple

  *go → **went*** *have → **had*** *see → **saw***

- for a list of irregular verbs, see page 80

Past simple of *be*: affirmative and negative

1 Complete the text with *was, wasn't, were* or *weren't*.

My parents **1** ___*were*___ **(+)** both born in 1977, but they **2** ________ **(–)** born in the same country. My mother **3** ________ **(+)** born in Valencia in Spain and my dad **4** ________ **(+)** born in Liverpool. Mum **5** ________ **(+)** a doctor in England and they **6** ________ **(+)** in the same hospital. But Dad **7** ________ **(–)** a doctor or a nurse: he **8** ________ **(+)** a patient and Mum **9** ________ **(+)** his doctor!

Past simple of *be*: *Yes*/*No* questions and short answers

2 Complete the questions with *was* or *were*.

1 ___*Were*___ Freya's parents born in the same year?
2 ________ they born in the same country?
3 ________ Freya's mother born in Madrid?
4 ________ her dad a doctor?
5 ________ her mother a doctor?

3 Write short answers for the questions in exercise 2. Use the information in the text in exercise 1.

1 *Yes, they were.*
2 ________
3 ________
4 ________
5 ________

Past simple of *be*: *Wh-* questions

4 Order the words to make questions.

1 the film / was / What time ?
What time was the film?
2 late / this morning / Why / you / were ?
____
3 the actors / Who / in the film / were ?
____
4 your / How much / new / were / jeans ?
____
5 parents / Where / last / were / your / night ?
____

Past simple of regular verbs: affirmative

5 Complete the table with the words in the box according to the spelling in the past simple.

~~call~~ chat dance decide plan play
receive stop study try want watch

+ *-ed*	+ *-d*	y + *-ied*	double consonant + *-ed*
called			

Past simple of regular and irregular verbs: affirmative

6 Complete the sentences with the correct past simple form of the verbs in the box.

be have leave meet
see ~~start~~ study visit win

1 I ___*started*___ at this school two years ago.
2 My mum ________ the Arsenal game on TV last night.
3 We ________ Turkey last year.
4 I ________ my best friend when I was three.
5 My friend and I ________ a lot for our exams.
6 We ________ a lot of homework at the weekend.
7 Our team ________ the school football competition.
8 The film ________ very bad so we ________ early.

Past simple: negative

- we form the past simple negative with *didn't* (*did not*) + infinitive
- the verb *didn't* is the same for all subject pronouns (*I, you, he, she, it, we, they*)

  *I **didn't** have any lunch.*

  *My mother **didn't** go to university.*

Past simple: questions and short answers

- we form past simple questions with *Did* + subject + infinitive
- we form short answers with *did* or *didn't*

  ***Did** you come by train?* *Yes, I **did**.*

  ***Did** he buy any oranges?* *No, he **didn't**.*
- to make *Wh-* questions, the order is question word (*Who, What*, etc.) + *did* + subject + infinitive

  Where did you see her? *What time did the class start?*

Superlative adjectives

- we use the superlative when we compare three or more things, to talk about the most or least extreme
- we use *the* before the superlative

  *He's **the tallest** in the class.*

  *It's **the coldest** day this year.*

Spelling: superlative adjectives

One-syllable adjectives	
add *-est*	tall – the tallest short – the shortest
Most one-syllable adjectives ending in consonant + vowel + consonant	
double final consonant and add *-est*	hot – the hottest thin – the thinnest
Two-syllable adjectives ending in -*y*	
change to *-iest*	heavy – the heaviest curly – the curliest
Adjectives with two or more syllables	
use *most* + adjective	boring – the most boring dangerous – the most dangerous
Irregular adjectives	
	good – the best bad – the worst

Past simple: negative

1 Complete the table.

Past simple	Infinitive
began	*begin*
did	
had	
left	
met	
told	
saw	
took	
won	

2 Complete the sentences with the underlined verb in the negative.

1 Greta took her camera to school, but she *didn't take* her laptop.
2 School began on 10th September, but football training ________ until 15th September.
3 I did my maths homework last night, but I ________ my English homework.
4 Mum told me to buy bread, but she ________ me to buy any fruit.
5 Clara left the party early, but Zoe ________ with her.
6 My brother's team won their match, but my team ________ our match.

Past simple: questions and short answers

3 Write questions to complete the dialogue.

Luke: Did 1 *you do your homework* yesterday?
Emma: No, I didn't. I'm doing my homework now.
Luke: Did 2 ________ early this morning?
Emma: No, I got up late. I was tired.
Luke: Why? Did 3 ________ Ben's party last night?
Emma: Yes, I did. The party was really good fun.
Luke: How did you get there? Did 4 ________ the underground?
Emma: No, I took a bus – it's quicker.
Luke: Did 5 ________ late?
Emma: Not really. I left the party at about 10:00 with Maria.

4 Complete the questions about Sally Ride, an astronaut. Ask questions about the underlined information.

1 *Where did she live* ?
She lived in California.
2 ________ ?
She studied at the University of California and Stanford University.
3 ________ ?
She played tennis. She was very good.
4 ________ ?
She studied physics.
5 ________ ?
She started studying to be an astronaut in 1978.
6 ________ ?
In 1983, she became the first American woman in space.

Superlative adjectives

5 Correct the sentences.

1 I think Arsenal is best team in the world.
I think Arsenal is the best team in the world.
2 Leon is the most tall boy in our class.
____
3 The elephant is the bigger animal on land.
____
4 In my city, the bus is the most bad way to travel.
____
5 This restaurant is most expensive in town.
____

6 Complete the questions with the superlative form of the adjective in brackets.

1 **Q:** Which is *the biggest* **(big)** continent?
A: Asia – it's four times bigger than the USA.
2 **Q:** Which is ________ **(small)** country?
A: Vatican City in Rome. Only 800 people live there!
3 **Q:** Which is ________ **(long)** group of mountains?
A: The Andes in South America.
4 **Q:** Which is ________ **(expensive)** country to live in?
A: Japan.
5 **Q:** Which is ________ **(tall)** mountain?
A: That's easy – it's Everest!

Describing a country

1 🔊30 **Complete the tourist information website about Jamaica with the words in the box. Listen and check.**

beach	capital	city	forest	mountain	river	sea	town	tree	village

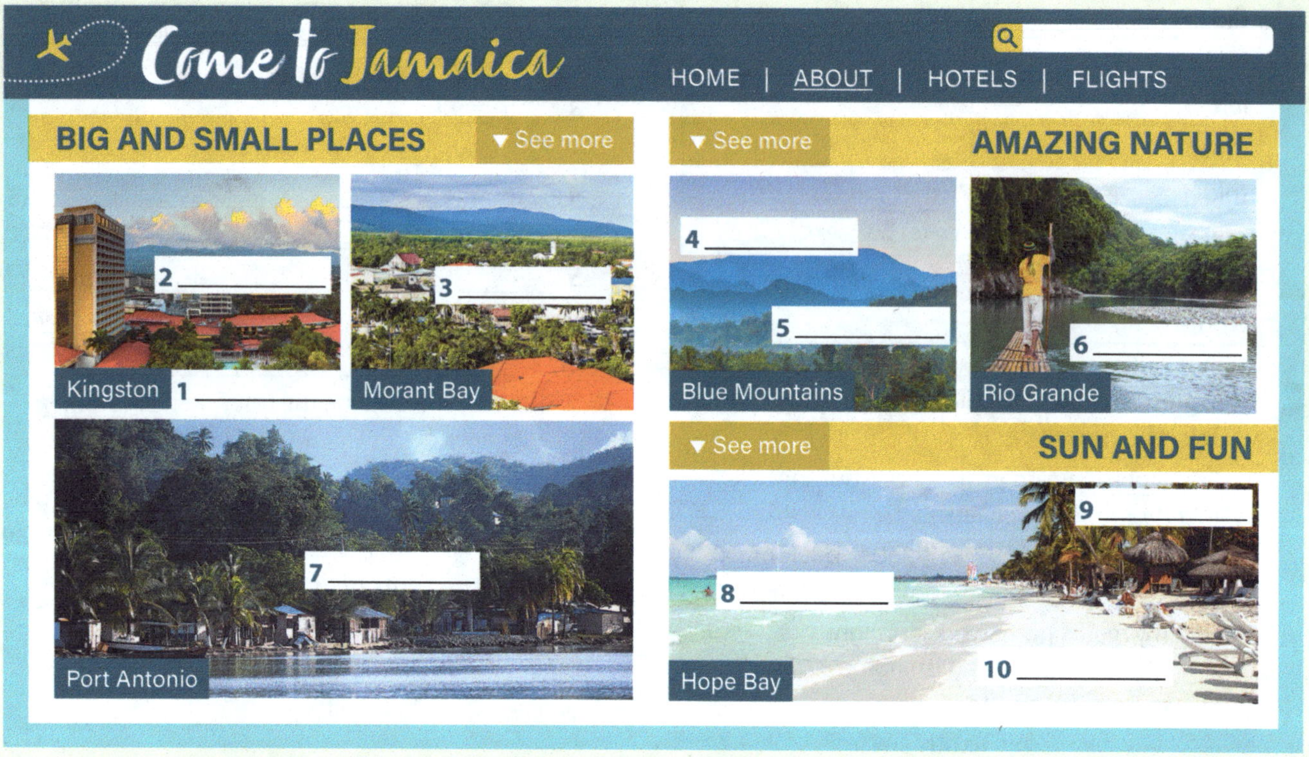

2 Match 1–6 with a–g. There is one extra phrase.

1 The Mediterranean
2 Seville
3 Copacabana
4 Sequoia
5 The Nile
6 The Himalayas

a mountains
b a river
c a forest
d a beach
e a sea
f a tree
g a city

3 What can you remember? Without looking at exercise 1, complete the sentences. Some words are in the plural.

1 Kingston is the ____________ of Jamaica. It's a big ____________.
2 Jamaica is in the Caribbean ____________.
3 The Rio Grande is a ____________.
4 Port Antonio is a ____________.
5 The Blue ____________ are in the centre of Jamaica.
6 Morant Bay is a ____________.
7 Hope Bay is a small town with a ____________.
8 Jamaica has got a big ____________ with lots of tall ____________ in the Blue Mountains.

4 Complete the text with information about your country.

The capital of my country is ____________. Two other important cities are ____________ and ____________. I'm from ____________: it's a ____________.

____________ and ____________ are two rivers in my country and ____________ is a mountain. My favourite beach is in ____________.

VOCABULARY CHALLENGE!

How many words can you complete in one minute?

1 s _ _
2 b _ _ ch
3 v _ ll _ g _
4 c _ p _ t _ l
5 r _ v _ r
6 f _ r _ st
7 m _ _ nt _ _ n

I don't feel well

1 31 **Label the picture with the words in the box. Listen and check.**

back	finger	head	stomach

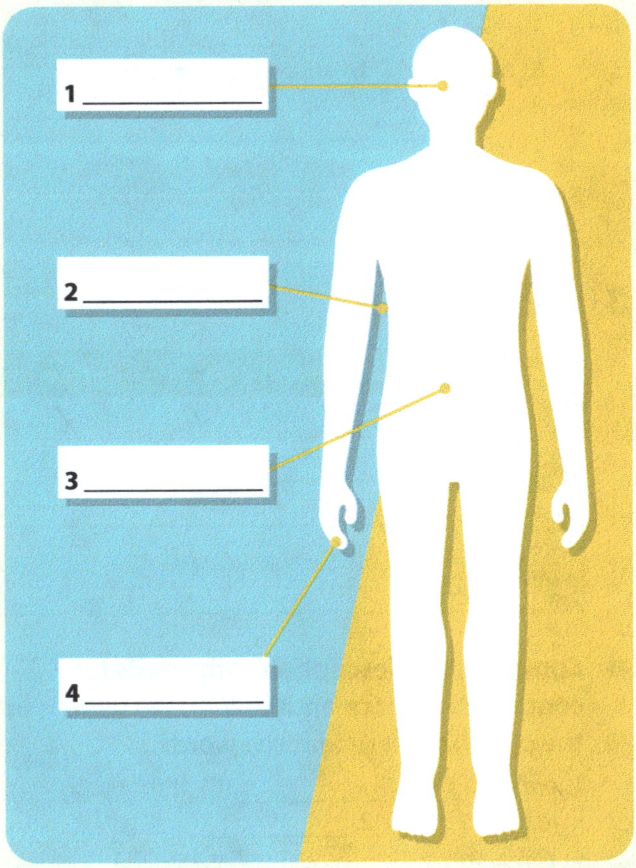

2 32 **Match the problems in the picture with the pictures. Listen, check and repeat.**

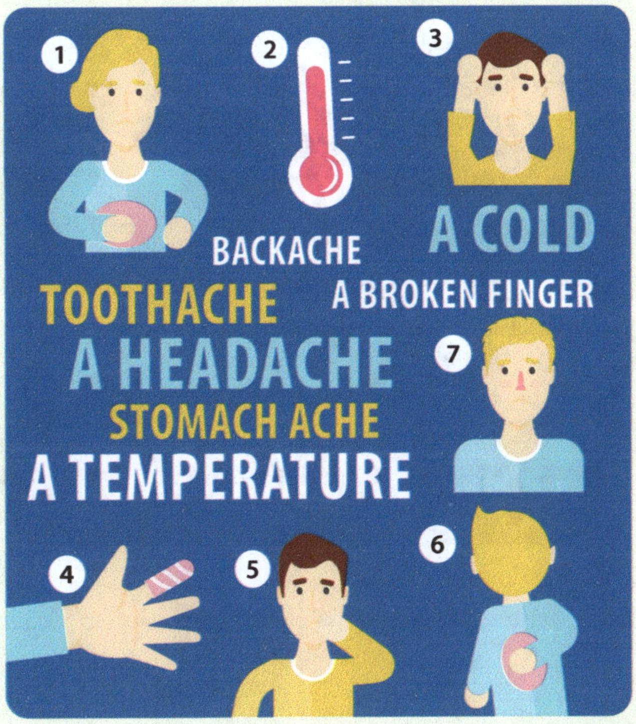

3 Complete the sentences.

What happens when … ?

1 you eat lots of chocolate and sweets
You get ____________ .
2 you eat spaghetti, three pizzas and four burgers
You get ____________ .
3 you play computer games for 14 hours
You get a ____________ .
4 you close the door on your hand
You get a ____________ .

4 Complete the dialogues with one of the problems.

1 **A:** I've got ____________ .
B: Go to the dentist.
2 I've got ____________ .
B: Do yoga.
3 I've got a ____________ of 39°C.
B: Take paracetamol.
4 I've got a ____________ .
B: Drink lots of water and eat oranges.

VOCABULARY CHALLENGE!

Can you find the seven health problems in two minutes?

S	T	A	Z	Q	R	S	S	B	B	C
T	E	M	P	E	R	A	T	U	R	E
O	D	E	F	P	R	S	O	G	O	H
O	J	I	K	L	A	B	M	M	K	N
T	O	C	O	L	D	P	A	Q	E	R
H	S	T	U	B	C	V	C	W	N	X
A	Y	E	A	R	A	C	H	E	F	A
C	Z	A	D	E	F	S	A	R	I	E
H	E	P	Q	U	R	A	C	O	N	P
E	B	A	C	K	A	C	H	E	G	I
H	E	A	D	A	C	H	E	C	E	K
E	R	I	N	G	A	R	M	K	R	X

Food containers and quantities

1 33 **Match photos 1–10 with the words in the box. Then listen and check.**

bag	bottle	bowl	can	cup
glass	kilo	litre	piece	slice

1 

2 

3 

4 

5 

6 

7 

8 

9 

10 

2 Find the word which is different in each group.

1 A piece of …
 a meat **b** water **c** chocolate
2 A bag of …
 a apples **b** shopping **c** fish
3 A bowl of …
 a biscuits **b** soup **c** rice
4 A kilo of …
 a cheese **b** oranges **c** sandwiches
5 A slice of …
 a coffee **b** bread **c** chicken

3 Complete the table.

	water	cola	coffee
A glass of …	✓	✓	✓
A cup of …			
A bottle of …			
A can of …			
A litre of …			

4 Complete the description with words for containers (C) or quantities (Q). One word is in the plural; don't repeat any words.

There's a big **1** ______________ **(C)** of shopping. In it, there's a small **2** ______________ **(C)** of water, two **3** ______________ **(C)** of cola and a **4** ______________ **(Q)** of oil. There's a **5** ______________ **(Q)** of rice and a small **6** ______________ **(Q)** of cheese.

VOCABULARY CHALLENGE!

How fast can you complete the table?

bag	bottle	bowl	can	cup
glass	kilo	litre	piece	slice

Used for liquids (e.g. water)	Not used for liquids

Time

1 🔊34 **Order the words in the box from short to long. Listen, check and repeat.**

century	day	hour	minute
month	second	week	year

1 ______ 5 ______
2 ______ 6 ______
3 ______ 7 ______
4 ______ 8 ______

2 🔊35 **Match seasons 1–4 with photos A–D. Listen and check.**

1 spring	Photo A
2 summer	Photo B
3 autumn	Photo C
4 winter	Photo D

3 Complete the missing words.

1. 60 ___*seconds*___ = 1 ___*minute*___
2. 100 ______ = 1 ______
3. 60 ______ = 1 ______
4. 12 ______ = 1 ______
5. 7 ______ = 1 ______
6. 24 ______ = 1 ______
7. 28, 30 or 31 ______ = 1 ______

4 Complete the sentences for you.

1. I take about ______ to do my homework.
2. I take about ______ to read a book.
3. I take about ______ to have lunch.
4. Our summer holidays usually last ______ .
5. Our winter holidays usually last ______ .

VOCABULARY CHALLENGE!

How many words can you write in the categories in two minutes?

1 less than a week

2 more than a day

3 seasons

Using technology

1 Complete the expressions with the verbs in the box.

copy	film	open	print	type	use

1 ____________ a tablet
2 ____________ an email
3 ____________ my friends singing
4 ____________ addresses from my old phone to my new phone
5 ____________ a new document
6 ____________ a ticket for my holiday

2 36 Match 1–6 with a–f to make mini dialogues. Listen and check.

1 **A:** That film's great!
2 **A:** I can't hear anything!
3 **A:** I'm on the train.
4 **A:** Have you got his phone number?
5 **A:** Can I use your laptop for my homework?
6 **A:** OK – finished!

a **B: Turn on** the speakers.
b **B: Text** me when you get to the station.
c **B:** Yes, I can **send** it to you.
d **B:** Remember to **save** the document.
e **B:** I can **download** it for you.
f **B:** Yes, but **turn** it **off** when you finish.

3 Choose the correct option.

How to **1 print/film** a document

2 Turn off/Turn on the computer and **3 open/download** a new document. **4 Text/Type** the information. **5 Use/Save** the document, then **6 send/copy** it to the printer.

4 Complete the questions with the verbs in the box. There are two extra verbs. Then answer the questions for you.

download	film	print	send	text	turn off

1 Do you ____________ your photos?
____
2 Do you ____________ your phone when you do your homework?
____
3 Do you ____________ music from the internet?
____
4 Do you normally ____________ emails or text messages?
____

VOCABULARY CHALLENGE!

Can you complete the crossword in three minutes?

Parts of a house or flat

1 37 **Match the words in the box with A–E. Listen and check.**

door garage gate path roof

2 38 **Match words 1–5 with photos A–E. Listen and check.**

1 a lift	Photo A
2 a floor	Photo B
3 entrance	Photo C
4 stairs	Photo D
5 exit	Photo E

3 39 **Listen to the sounds and complete the description of Ben's journey.**

Ben goes out of the **1** ____________ of his flat. The **2** ____________ isn't working, so he goes down the **3** ____________. He goes out of the **4** ____________ and walks along the street. At Abi's house, he opens the small, white **5** ____________ and walks up the **6** ____________ in the garden to Abi's front **7**____________.

4 Answer the questions for you.

1 Do you live in a flat or a house?

____

2 How many floors are there?

____

3 Is there a lift?

____

4 What colour is your front door?

____

5 Have you got a garden?

____

VOCABULARY CHALLENGE!

How fast can you complete the words?

1 p __ th

2 d __ __ r

3 g __ r __ g __

4 l __ ft

5 g __ rd __ n

6 r __ __ f

7 st __ __ rs

8 __ ntr __ nc __

Places where people work

1 40 **Match photos A–E with the words in the box. Listen and check.**

a farm a stadium a theatre an airport an office

A

____

B

____

C

____

D

____

E

____

2 41 **Match definitions 1–5 with the words in the box. Listen and check.**

a factory a health centre a post office a restaurant a shop

1 A place where people make things, e.g. cars __________
2 A place where you buy things __________
3 A place where you send letters __________
4 A place where a doctor works __________
5 a place where people pay to eat __________

3 Write the jobs.

1 I work on a farm and I spend my day with animals. __________

2 I work in a health centre and I see people who are ill. __________

3 I work in the evening. I do my job in a theatre. __________

4 I work in the kitchen of a big restaurant. __________

4 Complete the sentences for you.

1 My mum/dad/uncle/aunt works in a __________.
2 I'd like to work in a __________.
3 I don't want to work in a __________.

VOCABULARY CHALLENGE!

Can you complete the puzzle with the places where people work in three minutes? Which place is missing?

Travelling

1 42 **Read the definitions and match the words with photos A–F. Listen and check.**

A

____

B

____

C
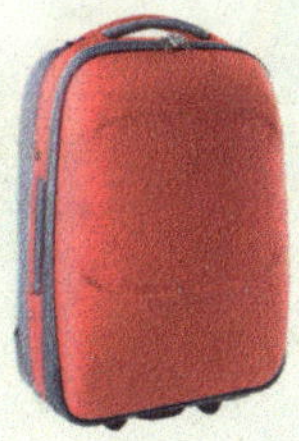
____

D

____

E

____

F

____

passport: an identity document you use when you travel to other countries

purse: women (usually) use this to put money in

wallet: men (usually) use this for paper money and credit cards

handbag: a small bag for money, keys, etc., usually used by a woman

suitcase: you put your clothes in this when you go on a holiday

guidebook: a book with information about a city or country

2 43 **Complete the sentences with the words in the box. Listen and check.**

document	driving licence	luggage	map

1 Leave the suitcases and bags. We can take the __________ to your room for you.
2 I always use the __________ on my phone when I can't find where I am.
3 I passed my test and now I can have a __________.
4 Before you leave the plane, please complete this travel __________ with your information.

3 Match sentences 1–4 with items a–d.

1 I have too many suitcases. Can you help me carry them?
2 Sorry, you can't come into the UK without it.
3 I want to learn all about the history of this city.
4 How do I get to the museum?

a guidebook
b passport
c map
d luggage

4 Answer the questions for you.

1 Do you prefer to use a real map or the map on your phone?
____
2 What things do you take when you travel?
____
3 Have you got a passport?
____
4 How many people have a driving licence in your family?
____

VOCABULARY CHALLENGE!

Can you recognise the objects in these photos in one minute?

1

____

2

____

3

____

4

____

A keypal message

Start with a friendly greeting

Remember to use capital letters

Zuza 2010

Hi there!

My name's Zuzanna. I'm 12.

I'm from Kazimierz Dolny in Poland. It's a small town, but it's very beautiful.

I live with my mum and dad and my brother, Filip. My dad's from Germany. I speak Polish, German and a little English.

In my free time, I like listening to music and playing basketball.

I want to meet people from different countries and practise my English. Please write and tell me about you and your family, your town and your hobbies.

Posted: Wednesday

Use a separate paragraph for different types of information

Tell the readers what you want to know

1 Read Zuzanna's message. Are the sentences T (true) or F (false)? Correct the false sentences.

1 Zuzanna is 12. ___

____

2 Kazimierz Dolny is a Polish city. ___

____

3 Her brother's name is Filip. ___

____

4 Zuzanna is German. ___

____

5 She likes playing music. ___

____

6 She wants to have friends from other countries. ___

____

2 Add capital letters to the text.

hi!

my name's heiko and i'm from austria. we live in the capital, vienna. i go to an american school, so i speak german and english. my best friend is manuel – he's from chile.

Hi!

____

____

____

____

____

3 Choose the correct option.

1 New York is a very **quiet/noisy** city.

2 I live in Paris – the capital of **French/France**.

3 My mother's **Spain/Spanish**.

4 Venice is a very **ugly/beautiful** city in Italy.

5 My grandparents are from **Russia/Russian**.

6 The centre of London is normally very **crowded/empty**.

4 Complete the dialogue with the words in brackets and the correct form of *be*. Use contractions where possible.

Karin: Hi. Where **1** ____________ **(you / ?)** from?

João: **2** ____________ **(we / +)** from Rio de Janeiro.

Karin: **3** ____________ **(Rio / ?)** the capital of Brazil?

João: No, **4** ____________ **(it / –)**. It's a big city, but it isn't the capital. The capital **5** ____________ **(Brasilia / +)**.

Karin: **6** ____________ **(Rio / ?)** on the sea?

João: Yes, **7** ____________ **(it / +)**. The **8** ____________ **(beaches / +)** fantastic!

Task

Write a keypal message to introduce yourself and find a keypal.

SKILLS BOOST

THINK

Which information do you want to include in your message? Choose five things and write notes.

Your name and age · A physical description · Your town or city · The weather in your town · Your friends/family · Free-time activities · Your heroes · Who you want to meet and what you want to know

____

____

____

____

PREPARE

Organise your ideas into paragraphs and write notes.

Paragraph 1: ____

Paragraph 2: ____

Paragraph 3: ____

Paragraph 4: ____

Paragraph 5: ____

WRITE

Write your keypal message. Use your notes and the message on p108 to help you.

____

____

____

____

____

____

____

____

CHECK

Read your message. Answer the questions.

1 Do you use a friendly greeting? ☐
2 Do you use capital letters? ☐
3 Do you use a separate paragraph for each type of information? ☐
4 Do you tell the readers what you want to know? ☐

Useful language

- Hi!/Hi there!
- I'm/My name's (Gemma).
- I'm from (London).
- It's a (quiet/noisy/interesting …) place.
- I live with (my mum).
- I like (sport).
- I want to meet people …

An email

Refer to the last email you got

Say where people are in the photo

Remember to use apostrophes

Finish with something you want to know

To: Manuel

About: Family photo

Hi Manuel,

In your last email, you asked about my family. Here's a photo.

My sister, Olivia, is on the left. She's tall with dark, straight hair. She's 17 and she goes to my school. She likes music and she plays the guitar and clarinet.

My brother, Adie, is in the middle. He's got short, dark hair and brown eyes. He's 15 and he loves video games.

The other girl is my cousin, Bella. She's 13. She's not from London. Bella's family are from Edinburgh.

In your next email, send me a picture of your family.

Best wishes,

Daniel

1 **Read Daniel's email and write D (Daniel), A (Adie), B (Bella) or O (Olivia).**

1 This person is 17. ___
2 This person's got brown eyes. ___
3 This person likes music. ___
4 This person lives in Scotland. ___
5 This person is 13 years old. ___
6 This person's got a brother and a sister. ___

2 **Add apostrophes to the sentences.**

1 Hes got long, brown hair.
____
2 My sisters best friend is 17.
____
3 My cousins havent got any pets.
____
4 My best friends house is near the sea.
____
5 My grandparents house isnt in our city.
____
6 My uncles hair is dark and hes got blue eyes.
____

3 **Complete the sentences with a part of the body.**

1 My friend's got curly ____________ .
2 My mother's got blue ____________ .
3 My sister's got a big ____________ in the middle of her face.
4 My grandfather's hair is dark, but his moustache and ____________ are white.

4 **Complete the dialogue with the correct form of *have got*. Use contractions where possible.**

Lucille: **1** ____________ any brothers and sisters?
Martin: Yes, **2** ____________ two sisters, Lisa and Karen.
Lucille: **3** ____________ brown hair like you?
Martin: No, **4** ____________ . We look very different. Karen **5** ____________ fair hair and Lisa **6** ____________ black hair.

Task

Find a photo of your family and describe the people in it.

THINK

Make notes.

1 Who are you going to write about? Include three people.

____

____

2 For each person, write notes about:

their age ______________________

their appearance ______________________

the things they like doing ______________________

PREPARE

Organise your ideas into paragraphs and write notes about each one.

Paragraph 1: Introduction ______________________

____

Paragraph 2: Description of ______________________

____

____

Paragraph 3: Description of ______________________

____

____

Paragraph 4: Description of ______________________

____

____

Paragraph 5: Something I'd like to know

____

____

WRITE

Write your email. Use your notes and the email on p110 to help you.

____

____

____

____

____

____

____

____

CHECK

Read your email. Answer the questions.

1 Do you refer to Daniel's email? ☐
2 Do you use apostrophes correctly? ☐
3 Do you say where people are in the photo? ☐
4 Do you finish with something you want to know? ☐

Useful language

- Hi!/Hi there!
- In your last email, you asked about …
- on the left/on the right/in the middle
- She's my (mother/sister …).
- He's got (blue eyes/brown hair …).
- He's (12/15 years old).
- She likes (sport).
- In your next email, …

A blog post

CASTLEPOINT

HOME | ABOUT | LOG IN

Say what the blog post is about in your first sentence

Castlepoint Shopping Park in Bournemouth is my favourite shopping centre.

Use clear headings for each paragraph

GETTING THERE

It's easy to get to Castlepoint by bus and there's a big car park. We normally go by car.

Give practical information for visitors

OPENING HOURS

The shops are open from 9:00 am to 8:00 pm, but on Sundays they open from 10:00 am to 4:30 pm.

SHOPS

There are lots of clothes and shoe shops and there's also a bookshop, a games shop and a big chemist's.

Use 'and' and 'but' to connect your ideas

FOOD AND DRINK

If you're hungry after all that shopping, it's not a problem. There are cafés and restaurants and you can meet your friends for pizza or a snack.

1 Read the blog post and underline the things there are at Castlepoint.

a car park cafés cinemas clothes shops food stalls good opening hours open Sunday evening public transport restaurants station

2 Complete the sentences with *and* or *but*.

1 It's open on Saturdays ____________ not on Sundays.
2 You can buy food in cafés ____________ restaurants.
3 There's a games shop ____________ there isn't a phone shop.
4 My mum likes shopping malls, ____________ Dad prefers to shop online.
5 There are two baker's ____________ a lot of food stalls.
6 My friends and I meet there ____________ go to the cinema.

3 Where can you buy these things?

1 pens, pencils and notebooks ____________
2 bread, biscuits and cakes ____________
3 a cup of tea and a sandwich ____________
4 cheese, potatoes and chicken ____________

4 Order the sentences to make a dialogue.

a Is there a shopping centre near your house? __
b Is it a good place to meet your friends? __
c Yes, there is. There's one about five minutes from here. __
d It's OK. There are some cafés, but there isn't a cinema. __
e Yes, there are. It's a good place to go shopping for clothes. __
f That's great! Are there a lot of shops? __

Task

Write a blog post about a place where you like to go shopping.

SKILLS BOOST

THINK

Decide what to include in your blog.

ENTERTAINMENT
INTRODUCTION
SHOPS
GETTING THERE
CAR PARKS
FOOD AND DRINK
MY FAVOURITE SHOP
OPENING HOURS

PREPARE

Write notes about what to include in each part of your blog post.

Section 1: ____________________

____

Section 2: ____________________

____

Section 3: ____________________

____

Section 4: ____________________

____

WRITE

Write your blog post. Use your notes and the blog post on p112 to help you.

____

____

____

____

____

____

____

____

CHECK

Read your blog post. Answer the questions.

1 Do you have an introduction? ☐
2 Do you use clear headings? ☐
3 Do you include practical information? ☐
4 Do you connect your ideas with *and* and *but*? ☐

Useful language

- My favourite …
- There is/There are …
- It's easy to get to …
- It's open from (X) to (Y).
- There are some/lots of …
- It's got …
- You can go by car/meet your friends.

Notes and messages

1

Use a greeting at the start of your message

Hi Tania,
Please buy some bread when you come home from school. We haven't got any at home.
Thanks.
Mum

Hey Mum!
No problem.
See you later.
T

It's OK to use short phrases

2

Hey Ray,
Is it OK to meet on Sunday, not Saturday? We've got a special lunch with all the family because it's my dad's birthday on Saturday. I hope it's not a problem.
Archie

Use 'because' to give reasons

Hi there,
That's fine. See you on Sunday.
Ray

Use an expression to finish your message

3

Hello Max,
Do you want to come to my house and play video games this afternoon?
Kiera

Hi Kiera,
Thanks, but I've got a guitar lesson. Sorry.
Max

1 Match notes and messages 1–3 with situations a–d. There is one situation you don't need.

a An invitation ___

b One person asks someone to do something ___

c A question about homework ___

d A change of plans ___

2 Connect the sentences with *because*. Think carefully about the order.

1 You've got an exam tomorrow. Come home early.

____

____

2 I have lunch at home. I live five minutes from school.

____

____

3 I'm busy on Saturday mornings. I go shopping with my parents.

____

____

4 We haven't got any. Please buy some fruit.

____

____

5 I meet my friends on Saturdays. On Sundays we go to my grandmother's house.

____

____

3 Complete the sentences with the verbs in the box.

have meet play sleep take

1 On Saturdays, I ____________ my friends at the shopping mall.

2 My best friend and I ____________ photos and post them on Instagram.

3 I ____________ basketball at school.

4 We ____________ breakfast at 9:00.

5 I ____________ about seven hours a night.

4 Complete the dialogue with the correct form of the verbs in brackets or a short answer.

A: **1** ______________________ **(your parents / do)** any sport?

B: Yes, **2** ______________________ **(they)**. They both **3** ______________________ **(like)** sport. My mum **4** ______________________ **(play)** hockey and my dad **5** ______________________ **(play)** tennis.

A: And your brother? **6** ______________________ **(play)** football?

B: No, **7** ______________________ **(he)**. He prefers music. He **8** ______________________ **(play)** the piano and the guitar.

Task

Write messages to friends.

THINK

Choose three of these situations:

a question about homework
an invitation
ask someone to do something
a change of plans
a friend's birthday
a special day at school

PREPARE

For each situation, decide who is writing and what the message is about.

1 Who is writing?

____

What is the message about?

____

2 Who is writing?

____

What is the message about?

____

3 Who is writing?

____

What is the message about?

____

4 Who is writing?

____

What is the message about?

____

WRITE

Write your messages. Use your notes and the examples on p114 to help you.

____
____
____
____
____
____
____
____

CHECK

Read your message. Answer the questions.

1 Do you use greetings? ☐
2 Do you use *because*? ☐
3 Do you use short phrases? ☐
4 Do you use an expression to finish your message? ☐

Useful language

- Hi/Hey/Hello.
- Thanks/See you later/See you tomorrow.
- It's (Dan's birthday/my party/my football match) on Saturday.
- Please buy … /Please come … /Please help …
- Do you want to … ?
- I hope that's OK/not a problem.

An advert

Use a heading at the start of your advert

THE POWER BANK CHARGER

Hockey practice finishes. Time to phone your mum to come and get you in the car, but – oh no! Your phone is dead! You can't call her!

Tell a story – it makes the advert more interesting

With a Power Bank Charger, this isn't a problem! You can charge your phone when you want and where you want. It's only 15 x 7.5 cm and at 350 grams, it's really light too. Put it in your bag and you can charge any time. The Power Bank Charger isn't only for phones: you can charge tablets too. And with two USB ports, you and your friend can both charge your phones at the same time.

The Power Bank Charger: don't leave home without it.

Include practical information

Have a final line people can remember

Check your spelling when you finish

1 **Read the advert and complete the table with information or write *Don't know*.**

Name	
How big?	
What colours?	
How heavy?	
Number of USB ports?	
Price?	

2 **Correct the spelling of one word in the sentences.**

1 This camra is really small and light.
____

2 I don't think the keybord is easy to use.
____

3 My dad's tablet is heavyer than mine.
____

4 Is it dificult to use the touchpad?
____

5 Your phone's screan is a lot bigger than mine.
____

6 This computer is fastter than the one in our class.
____

3 **Complete the sentences with the adjectives in the box.**

cheap	difficult	easy	expensive	heavy	slow

1 This game only costs €10. It's very ______________ .

2 The instructions for this exercise are ______________ . I don't understand them.

3 My parents don't want to buy me a new guitar. They say it's too ______________ .

4 Our English homework today is ______________ . We can finish it in five minutes.

5 Don't walk to school, it's very ______________ . We can go by bike.

6 Can you help me carry these books? They're very ______________ .

4 **Write a new sentence that means the same as the first with the opposite adjective.**

1 The laptop is heavier than the tablet.
The tablet ______________________________ .

2 The black camera is cheaper than the white camera.
The white camera ______________________________
______________________________ .

3 Mum's computer is faster than Dad's.
Dad's computer ______________________________
______________________________ .

4 Your camera is more difficult to use than mine.
My camera ______________________________ .

Task

Write an advert.

SKILLS BOOST

THINK

Choose one of the objects.

a camera
a phone
a tablet
a speaker
a laptop

PREPARE

Make notes in the table with information about the object.

Name	
How big?	
What colours?	
How heavy?	
Price?	
Other information	

WRITE

Write your advert. Use your notes and the example on p116 to help you.

____
____
____
____
____
____
____
____

CHECK

Read your message. Answer the questions.

1 Do you use a heading? ☐
2 Do you tell a story? ☐
3 Do you give practical information? ☐
4 Do you use a final line that people can remember? ☐

Useful language

- It can (take great photos, go in your bag …).
- It's very (light, small, easy to use).
- It's (smaller, easier, faster) than …
- It's perfect for (students, people who travel …).
- It comes with (a case, a charger …).
- It's only (€30).

Text messages

1 Read the text messages. Are the sentences T (true) or F (false)? Correct the false sentences.

1 Ben is doing his homework. ___

____

2 Logan is at the skate park. ___

____

3 Jimmy is Logan's brother. ___

____

4 Ben thinks Jimmy is a good cook. ___

____

5 They agree to meet after Ben eats. ___

____

2 Connect the sentences with *so*.

1 I can't meet now. I'm doing my homework.

____

2 It's raining. We're watching a film at home.

____

3 We're having a special dinner. It's Dad's birthday.

____

4 She's not in school today. Our teacher's ill.

____

5 We haven't got any money. We're watching TV.

____

3 Complete the sentences with a room.

1 Mum's making lunch in the ______________ .
2 Peter's having a shower in the ______________ .
3 Maura's lying on the bed in her ______________ .
4 My dad's watching TV in the ______________ .
5 I'm preparing the table for lunch in the ______________ .

4 Complete the dialogue with the verbs in brackets in the present continuous.

Abi: What **1** ______________________ **(you/do)**?
Flo: It's a typical Sunday morning in our house. I **2** ______________________ **(listen)** to music in bed and Ciara **3** ______________________ **(sleep)**.
Abi: What about your parents? **4** ______________________ **(they/sleep)**?
Flo: No, they aren't. Mum **5** ______________________ **(do)** some work and Dad **6** ______________________ **(make)** lunch. What about you?

Task

Write a text message dialogue.

SKILLS BOOST

THINK

1 Choose two people.

a two friends
b two people in the same family

2 Choose a subject.

a ask to meet
b ask for help

PREPARE

Make a plan for your conversation. Don't write complete sentences.

A: Say hello. What / doing?
B: Homework. You?
A: Watch TV ...

____
____
____

WRITE

Write your text message dialogue. Use your notes and the example on p118 to help you.

____
____
____
____
____
____
____
____
____
____
____

CHECK

Read your messages. Answer the questions.

1 Do you use letters as words? ☐
2 Do you use *so* to explain results? ☐
3 Do you miss out words? ☐
4 Do you use punctuation to show how you feel? ☐

Useful language

- Hello / Hi.
- How R U? What R U doing? C U later.
- Are you busy? / Are you free?
- Can you help me with … ? / Can you meet?
- Sorry, but I'm studying. / Sorry, I'm having dinner.
- OK, see you later. / See you there.

A description of a fictional character

Introduce the character in the opening sentence

My favourite fictional character is Sam Gardner from the Netflix series *Atypical*.

Give information about the character

Sam is a student in high school in the United States, and he lives with his parents and his younger sister, Casey, who is very good at sport. At first, you think it is a typical American family with a mother, a father and two teenage children, but there's an important difference: Sam is autistic.

Use 'also' to give more information

Sam is different from other teenagers. He's an expert on Antarctica, but he is very direct and he also finds it difficult to understand how other people feel.

Say why you like the character

I like Sam because he shows us how people who are autistic see the world and helps us understand people who are different.

1 Read the description and match 1–6 with a–f to make sentences.

1 Sam is
2 Sam lives with
3 Sam's sister is
4 Sam isn't
5 Sam's interested in
6 It's difficult for Sam to

a the same as other teenagers.
b American.
c understand people.
d his parents and his sister.
e good at sport.
f Antarctica.

2 Add the word *also* to the sentences.

1 Sam goes to school and he works in a computer shop.

____

2 Sam likes Antarctica and he loves penguins.

____

3 He doesn't like noisy places and he doesn't like cats.

____

4 He's good at maths and he can remember a lot of information.

____

5 Sam's best friend is Zahid and Sam's got a girlfriend called Paige.

____

3 The words in bold are in the wrong sentence. Correct the sentences.

1 I'm very **hungry**. Can you get me a drink?

____

2 Don't look so **interested**. I'm sure your exam was fine.

____

3 After two hours in the gym, I was very **thirsty**.

____

4 I'm **tired**. Why don't we get something to eat?

____

5 Jan's not **worried** in this series so he's watching something in his room.

____

4 Complete the dialogue with *was*, *were*, *wasn't* or *weren't*.

A: What **1** ____________ your favourite book when you **2** ____________ a child?

B: There **3** ____________ some books with one character I liked: Rowley Jefferson.

A: Who **4** ____________ the author?

B: The books **5** ____________ by a German writer called Knister. But that **6** ____________ his real name. The writer's name is Ludger Jochmann.

A: Why **7** ____________ they your favourite books?

B: Because they **8** ____________ very long, but the stories **9** ____________ very exciting.

Task

Write a description of a fictional character.

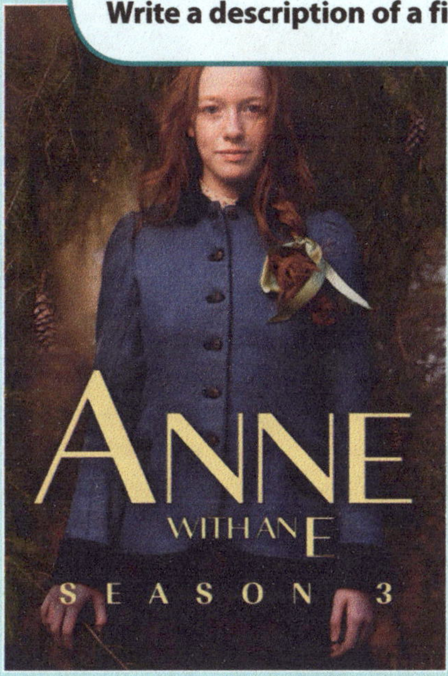

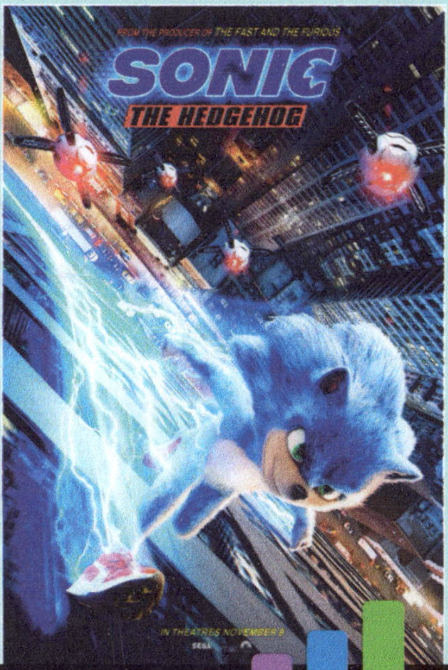

SKILLS BOOST

THINK

Think of characters from books, films, TV series or games and write your ideas in the table.

Books	Films	TV series	Games

PREPARE

Choose one of your characters. Make notes about the character. Include:

the name and the book, film, series or game the character is in

a description of the character (age, family, where they live)

more information about what makes the character special (likes and dislikes, abilities, etc.)

why you like this character

WRITE

Write your description. Use your notes and the example on p120 to help you.

CHECK

Read your description. Answer the questions.

1 Do you include an opening sentence to introduce the character? ☐
2 Do you include information about their life? ☐
3 Do you use *also* to give additional information? ☐
4 Do you say why you like the character? ☐

Useful language

- My favourite character is … from the book/series/film/game …
- He/She is …
- He/She was born in …
- Her father/mother was …
- I like … because …

A story

Get the reader's attention with your first line

Give some background information for your story

Use adjectives to describe the place

Use 'before' and 'after' to show the order of events in the story

Write a final idea to finish your story

The moment I got on the bus, I knew this was going to be a special day.

It was my first time in Morocco and we were on holiday in Marrakesh. Just three hours ago we were in London and now we were in a very different place. We were in Africa.

After we got on the airport bus, it took half an hour to get to the city centre. Immediately, everything was different. It was hot and noisy. We passed a motorbike with three people on it, including a grandmother with two big bags. Then we passed two men in traditional clothes on donkeys.

We arrived at Jemaa el-Fna, a square in the centre of Marrakesh. There were people everywhere. A woman passed, selling orange juice. Then a man walked by with a snake and I thought: I love this city.

1 Read the story and put the sentences in the correct order.

a They took a bus from the airport to the city centre. ___
b The writer felt very happy in the city. ___
c They left London. ___
d They saw a man with a snake. ___
e From the bus they saw people on a motorbike and on donkeys. ___
f They went to Marrakesh by plane. ___
g They arrived in the city centre. ___

2 Complete the sentences with *before* or *after*.

1 ______________ I got on the bus, I bought a ticket from the driver.
2 ______________ the film finished, we walked home.
3 ______________ my mother started driving, we closed the car doors.
4 ______________ the bus arrived, we waited in a queue for about 40 minutes.
5 ______________ the cars stopped, we crossed the road.

3 Complete the sentences with a verb.

1 It isn't a long journey, so we can ______________ on foot.
2 If you don't want to drive, we can ______________ the bus.
3 Remember to ______________ your ticket before you get on the train.
4 Excuse me, I want to ______________ the bus at the next stop.
5 Do any of your friends ______________ their bike to school?

4 Complete the text with the affirmative or negative form of the verbs in brackets.

Last July, my friend **1** ______________ **(ask / +)** me to go to her village. We **2** ______________ **(arrive / +)** on Friday afternoon and we **3** ______________ **(go / +)** to the swimming pool to meet her friends. I **4** ______________ **(be / +)** a bit nervous because I **5** ______________ **(know / –)** anyone, but they **6** ______________ **(be / +)** all very friendly. The next day, there **7** ______________ **(be / +)** a special party and I **8** ______________ **(take / +)** a lot of photographs. The day we **9** ______________ **(leave / +)**, I was very sad. I **10** ______________ **(want / –)** to say goodbye.

Task

Write a story about travelling.

THINK

The first sentence of the story is:

The moment I got on the ... ,
I knew ...

Decide how to complete the story.

PREPARE

Make notes about your story. Think about:

how you travelled

___

where you came from and where you went

___

what was special or unusual

___

how you felt

___

WRITE

Write your story. Use your notes and the example on p122 to help you.

___

CHECK

Read your story. Answer the questions.

1. Do you get the reader's attention with the opening sentence? ☐
2. Do you include background information? ☐
3. Do you use adjectives? ☐
4. Do you use *before* and *after*? ☐
5. Does your story have a good ending? ☐

Useful language

- It was my first time in ...
- Before we ... , / After we ... ,
- When we (arrived) ...
- We travelled by (bus/train/plane)/on foot.
- It took (half an hour) to ...
- It was the best/worst day of my life.

1 Social and emotional competence

MAKING NEW PEOPLE FEEL WELCOME

We're all new sometimes. We begin a sport or activity, or maybe we move to a different town or country and start at a new school. It's not easy to be new and to make friends in a new place. That's why it's important to include new people and make them feel welcome.

1 Look at the two photos. Marcia and Leila are both new. Which words in the box describe how each girl feels?

happy	lonely	part of a group	sad

Marcia: ______________________________

Leila: ______________________________

2 Match words and phrases 1–5 with definitions a–e.

1 move
2 make friends
3 begin
4 include
5 make someone feel welcome

a meet new people and start to be friends with them
b start
c leave one place and go to live in another place
d show a new person you are happy they are here
e make someone part of a group or activity

3 Complete what the girls in the photos are thinking with words from exercise 2.

Marcia: 'I'm making lots of new ____________ . Everyone here is making me feel very ____________ .'

Leila: 'Why did my family ____________ to this new town? Why don't the other students ____________ me?'

4 Read the two diary entries on p125. Marcia and Leila are writing about their first day at school. Which diary entry relates to each person?

5 Write *Leila*, *Marcia* or *Both*.

1 I feel nervous because tomorrow is my first day.
____

2 I miss friends from my old school.
____

3 I don't have any new friends.
____

4 I have a new friend from a different place.
____

5 I'm happy after my first day.
____

6 Look at the example and then complete the table with notes about an experience you had.

	Example	You
A situation when you were new	*My first day in the swimming club*	
Your feelings before	*Very nervous. I didn't know anyone.*	
New people	*Marlon and Toby – very friendly*	
Situation now	*I have lots of friends.*	

7 Tick (✓) three ideas from the list that you can do next time a new person comes to your class, to make them feel welcome.

- begin a conversation with them and ask their name ☐
- ask if they need help ☐
- sit with them in class ☐
- give them your phone number ☐
- talk to them in the playground ☐
- include them in your conversations ☐

1

10th SEPTEMBER

5:00 AM

I can't sleep. I feel very nervous about moving to this city and starting at the new school.

7:30 PM

I don't like the new school. I'm the only new person in the class. All the other students are in big groups of friends. There's no one sitting with me. They don't want to talk to me. I don't think they like me.

2

10th September

7:00 am

My first day at the new school. I'm happy but also a bit nervous. I don't know anyone. I really miss my friends from Garrett Street school.

8:45 pm

Well the first day was OK! The other people in my class are really nice. They're very friendly and helped me with all the new things. I sit next to Sophie. She's from Nigeria. She also plays basketball and comes home on the same bus as me ...

UNDERSTANDING WHY THE PEOPLE AROUND US ARE IMPORTANT

We have lots of people around us: family, friends, teammates and neighbours. Our friends and families love us and understand us. When we have problems, different people help us in different ways. They also influence our ideas and help us understand other opinions.

1 Read the introduction. Which sentence is the best summary?

- **a** Only people in our family are important.
- **b** All people around us are important but not in the same way.
- **c** It's important to be the same as the people around us.

2 Read and complete the Q & A with the words in the box.

different ideas neighbours problems

FAMILY AND FRIENDS Q & A

Who are the people around us?

They include family, friends and
1 ____________.

Why are they important?

These people are important for us in
2 ____________ ways.

When can they help us?

When we have 3 ____________, we can ask different people for help.

What other things do they do?

Our family and friends also influence our
4 ____________.

3 Claude is writing about his family and friends. Read the texts on p127. Write the names of the people in the photos.

1 ____________
2 ____________
3 ____________
4 ____________
5 ____________

4 How and when does each person help Claude? Complete the table.

Who?	How and when do they help?
Marcos	
Jemima	
Lennie	
Mum	
Julian and Robby	

5 Which two people help Claude understand other people's ideas?

____

6 Think about yourself. Who do you talk to if … ?

1 you have a problem at home

____

____

2 you have a problem at school

____

____

3 you have a problem with a hobby or activity

____

____

7 Who do you help and when? Think of three examples.

1 ____________________________

____

2 ____________________________

____

3 ____________________________

____

1

2

3

4

MARCOS is my best friend, but we're very different. I love sport but he likes music. Because we're different, he helps me think about things in a new way.

JEMIMA is my sister. She's 14. We aren't interested in the same things, but if I don't understand my homework, she always helps me.

LENNIE is my uncle – my mum's brother. He loves sport, too. He's younger than my mum and I talk to him if I have problems at home. He's a very good listener and helps me understand Mum and Jemima.

MUM is – Mum! We don't agree about some things, for example, what time I go to bed or when I can play computer games. But she always helps me and makes time to talk to me.

JULIAN AND ROBBY are in my ice hockey team. If I have a bad day at training or I play badly in a match, they understand.

5

THINKING ABOUT WHAT YOU EAT

It's a good idea to eat a balance of different food to be healthy. Be open to trying new food because it helps you understand people from different places. Some people say 'You are what you eat', so it's important to think about the food you eat.

1 Read the 'Thinking about what you eat' introduction and complete the sentences.

1 If you are an ____________ person, you are happy to think about ideas that are different.

2 It's important to have a ____________ between time to study and time for sport and hobbies.

3 To be ____________ , do sport, sleep eight hours a night and eat good food.

2 Complete the Top Tips with the phrases in the box.

Eat a balance of different food Eat healthy food Try something new

TOP TIPS FOR EATING WELL

A ______________________ : Don't eat a lot of fast food like burgers, pizzas and chips and a lot of sweets and snacks.

B ______________________ : Try to have some protein (meat, fish, tofu, beans), carbohydrates (rice, pasta, potatoes) and lots of fruit and vegetables.

C ______________________ : Eat some of a vegetable you think you don't like or try food from a different country.

3 Read the infographic. Which section is about … ?

1 trying different food ___

2 the problems of fast food ___

3 healthy eating ___

4 Find words in the infographic which mean …

1 a white drink (section A) ____________

2 a part of the body (section A) ____________

3 a meal (section A) ____________

4 something you use to eat ice cream or soup (section B) ____________

5 a word which means 1,000,000,000 (section B) ____________

6 food you don't eat in a house or restaurant (section C) ____________

5 What about you? How many days a week do you … ?

1 have breakfast ____________

2 eat fast food ____________

3 eat fruit and vegetables ____________

4 drink cola or coffee ____________

5 eat meat ____________

6 Are you open to new things? For each thing, write 'I'll try it' or 'No way!'. Then read the box to discover if you are an open person.

- street food in a different country ____________
- a new fruit or vegetable ____________
- a typical meal from your friend's country ____________
- insects ____________
- a vegetarian or vegan meal ____________

How many times did you say 'I'll try it!'?

4–5 Fantastic! You're a very open person and you like new things.

2–3 OK! It's good you're open to trying some things.

0–1 Oh no! Try to be more open. The thing you try could be your new favourite dish!

7 Choose three of the food challenges to try this month, or write your own challenge.

- Eat five portions of fruit and vegetables every day.
- Try food from a different country.
- Don't eat fast food.
- Try a vegetarian meal.
- Eat ______________________
- Don't eat ______________________

YOU ARE WHAT YOU EAT

A

- Fruit, vegetables, meat and nuts are all great brain food.
- **31%** of 11-year-olds don't eat breakfast.
- Only **44%** of 11-year-olds eat fruit every day.
- Think when you drink. Don't choose cola or coffee! Orange juice and milk have got vitamins and minerals and are good for your body.

B

- Fast food has got a lot of sugar, salt and fat. It's easy and quick, but it's not good for you.
- There are 16 spoons of sugar in one 600 ml bottle of cola.
- **80%** of people eat fast food every day!
- Americans eat **13 billion** hamburgers every year.
- A typical German eats more than **11 kilos** of chocolate a year.

C

- When you go on holiday, try the local street food.
- If you have friends from other countries, ask to cook with them. It's easier to try something if you know how to make it.
- Start small: try a little of something new.

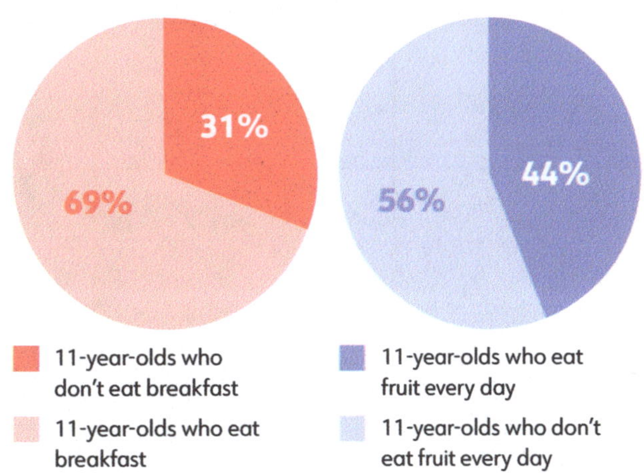

BEING ORGANISED

If you are organised, you can do more things with your time. So you can do all your schoolwork and you can also spend more time doing other things that you like!

1 Look at the expressions in bold in the box. Which one means … ?

1 the latest possible time
2 some paper pages or an app with days, weeks and months of the year
3 doesn't remember

> does things **at the last minute**
> **forgets** to do things makes a plan
> starts studying the day before an exam
> starts their homework at 10:00 pm
> studies a little every day uses a **calendar**
> uses different colour pens writes lists

2 Complete the table with the activities in the box in exercise 1.

An organised person …	A disorganised person …

3 Add one more idea to the table.

4 Read the tips on p131 and choose the best icon for each section.

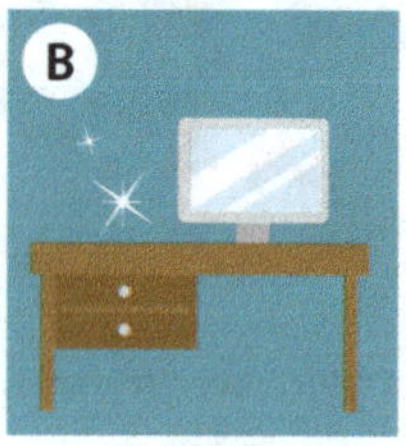

___ ___ ___

___ ___ ___

5 Match 1–6 with a–f to make sentences.

1 After half an hour working,
2 After you finish a job,
3 It's a good idea to number
4 Organise your clothes and bag
5 Prepare the place
6 Use colours for different

a before you go to bed.
b where you work.
c relax for a short time.
d types of activities on your plan.
e your jobs from most to least important.
f tick it on your list.

6 Which sentence goes with each tip?

Tip 1 ___ Tip 3 ___ Tip 5 ___
Tip 2 ___ Tip 4 ___ Tip 6 ___

7 Complete the sentences for you.

1 In general I'm **quite/very organised/disorganised**.
2 One good thing I do is ______________________
____
______________________.
3 To be more organised, I want to try to ______________________
____
______________________.

Organise your jobs

1. The first rule of being organised is to **write a 'to do' list.** It's important to know what you need to do. It's also great when you can tick things after you finish them!
2. When you have your 'to do' list, organise it. **Put the jobs in order** with the most important first and write when you need to do each thing.

Organise your time

3. **Make a plan** of your week or your weekend. Use different colours for free-time activities and for homework or studying.
4. People work better if they **take breaks.** Try to work hard for 30 minutes and then take a 5-minute break. Only look at your phone in your break!

Organise your things

5. Before you start, **organise the table where you work.** Make space for your books or computer. Have pens ready and always have something to drink.
6. **Prepare for school the night before.** Get your clothes out and pack your bag.

KNOWING WHAT YOU DO WELL AND WHAT YOU ENJOY

We're all good at some things and not so good at other things. It's important to know what you do well and work to improve other things. And remember, you don't need to be good at something to enjoy it.

1 **Read the examples, then write sentences for you with the phrases in bold and words in the box. Or you can use your own ideas.**

A 

I'm good at tennis.

I'm interested in computers.

B 

C 

I'm not good at maths.

SPORT MUSIC ART ENGLISH MATHS COOKING ACTING PLAYING THE GUITAR SINGING USING COMPUTERS TAKING PHOTOS

2 **Look at another word cloud. It includes different things people are good at. Match the sentences with one of the abilities in the box.**

BEING A GOOD FRIEND SAYING THANK YOU RELAXING HELPING OTHER PEOPLE RECYCLING AND RE-USING THINGS REMEMBERING THINGS BEING HEALTHY LISTENING TO PEOPLE BEING ORGANISED

1 What a fantastic present! Thank you.

____

2 Tell me about it.

____

3 I made this bag from my old jeans.

____

4 Don't forget it's Dan's birthday on Friday.

____

5 Can I help you make dinner?

____

3 **Are you good at more things in the first or the second word cloud?**

____

4 **Read the questionnaire on p133 and answer the questions.**

5 **Add up the points for your answers and then read *Who are you?* Do you agree with what it says?**

Question 1	**A:** 2	**B:** 1
Question 2	**A:** 1	**B:** 2
Question 3	**A:** 1	**B:** 2
Question 4	**A:** 2	**B:** 1
Question 5	**A:** 2	**B:** 1
Question 6	**A:** 1	**B:** 2
Question 7	**A:** 1	**B:** 2

WHO ARE YOU?

7–10 points: You like to try new things, and it's not important for you to be the best at something. But remember, it's also good to work hard and do things well.

11–14 points: You like to be good at things! Remember, it's also good to learn. Why not try something new, or ask a friend to teach you something they're good at?

6 **Complete the sentences for you.**

1 A new activity I'd like to try is ______________________________.

2 One thing I want to do better is ______________________________.

3 Something I'm not very good at but enjoy doing is ______________________________.

IS 'BEING GOOD' IMPORTANT TO YOU?

1. **Is it better to do ... ?**
   A one thing very well
   B four or five things not so well

2. **Think of something you are good at. Can you think of two people who do it better than you?**
   A Yes
   B No

3. **Do you like winning games and competitions in your hobbies?**
   A It's not that important.
   B Yes, and you're prepared to practise hard to win.

4. **Do you prefer to ... ?**
   A do things you know you can do well
   B try new things

5. **How do you feel when you try something new?**
   A Nervous, but you also want to try and be good at it quickly.
   B Interested, but if you don't like it, you don't need to continue.

6. **How do you feel when you do something you're not good at?**
   A It's not important, I just want to have fun!
   B I don't like it; I want to be the best.

7. **Do you prefer team sports or individual sports?**
   A Team sports – it's more fun to be with other people.
   B Individual sports, but team sports are good if everyone in the team works hard.

RESPECTING WHAT PEOPLE WEAR

Some people like to wear the same clothes as their friends. But it's not a problem if people look different or like different clothes. It's not a good idea to decide if you like a person or not because of what they wear. Think about the person, not their clothes!

1 Answer the questions for you.

1 Write the names of two people who wear similar clothes to you.

____

2 Write the names of two people who wear different clothes to you.

____

3 In general, do your friends look similar or different to you?

____

2 Complete the texts with the words in the box.

activity	comfortable	country
don't	friends	uniform

WHY DO SOME GROUPS OF TEENAGERS DRESS THE SAME?

Some people wear similar clothes because they do the same sport or **1** ____________ . Other teenagers wear a school **2** ____________ and some people wear similar clothes because they are from the same **3** ____________ . And some people just like looking the same as their **4** ____________ !

WHY DO SOME TEENAGERS DRESS DIFFERENTLY?

Some people like to wear different clothes because they think they are more **5** ____________ or practical. Some teenagers come from families that dress differently. And some people like being different: they **6** ____________ want to look the same as other people.

3 It's important to be open and friendly to all people, even if they look different. Which people are open? Which people are not?

'I don't want to talk to him. I think he looks strange and different.' **Lee**

'She's wearing very different clothes. I think that's really cool and interesting!' **Claire**

'His clothes are great! I'm going to say "Hello."' **Rex**

'What is she wearing?! She can't be in our group.' **Helena**

4 Read the blog on p135 and write the names of people who …

1 dress the same as their friends.

____

2 dress differently from their friends.

____

5 Read again and answer the questions with J (Jens), K (Kendall), M (Markus) or P (Patti). Sometimes more than one answer is correct.

1 Who has friends who always wear black clothes?

____

2 Who wears clothes because of the activity they do? __________

3 Who wears jeans? __________

4 Who wears the same clothes as their friends and has similar hair? __________

5 Who doesn't wear trainers or sports clothes?

____

6 Complete the sentences with your ideas.

1 It's not important to look the same, because

____

______________________________ .

2 It's good to have friends who look different, because

____

______________________________ .

3 The way people look isn't the most important thing. There are more important things, for example,

____

______________________________ .

Home | About | Archives | Questions

This week's question:

Do you dress the same as your friends?

Send us your answers with a photo.

Markus, 12, Copenhagen

I wear the same clothes as my friends. We all love skateboarding, so we wear clothes which are good for skating: jeans or trousers that you can move in and big, comfortable T-shirts. We don't wear the same clothes because we want to look the same. We wear them because they're easy to skate in.

Kendall, 12, St Louis

My friends and I all look a bit different. Marco and Felix always wear black. Jason, Sven and Carola all like sporty clothes. Ben has got yellow hair and he wears very big clothes, and I wear jeans every day – I don't think about clothes very much. The important thing is that we're all friends.

Jens, 11, Berlin

I don't look like my friends. They all wear sports clothes, but I don't like T-shirts and I never wear trainers. I always wear a shirt and jacket with black trousers. I don't want to look the same as other people. This is me! My friends like me: my clothes aren't important to them.

Patti, 12, Miami

My friends and I all have long hair and we always dress the same. I prefer people who look the same as me.

USING SOCIAL MEDIA CAREFULLY

When we use social media, it's important to think how other people feel. We don't want to post or share things which hurt other people or make them unhappy. The best rule is 'treat other people the way you want them to treat you'.

1 Answer the questions.

Do you use social media?

___

Which social media apps and platforms do you use?

___

Do you post or share information and photos about yourself or about other people?

___

2 Read the tips for using social media. Put them in order from 1 to 4 (1 = the best idea, 4 = the worst idea).

Tips for using **social media** carefully

1 Only post good things. ___
2 Think before you post or share. ___
3 Think before you join a social media group. ___
4 Don't post when you are angry. ___

3 Match a–d with 1–4 in exercise 2 to complete the tips.

a You can't always stop the message after you send it. ___
b Do you know all the other people? Do you want people who you don't know to see your photos? ___
c It's better to wait and, when you are calm, decide what to do. ___
d You can't hurt other people if you say positive things. ___

4 Read the comic on p137 and answer the questions.

1 Who is in the photo? ___
2 Who took the photo? ___
3 Who shares the photo with the class group? ___
4 Who is nice to Bruno? ___

5 Which two rules in the Tip box does Marina break?

___

___

6 Which of these things do you think are good and bad advice in Bruno's situation? Why?

1 Tell the teachers ___
2 Post bad things about Marina ___
3 Leave the class group ___
4 Tell your parents ___
5 Ignore it ___

7 Write three more tips for using social media carefully.

1 ___
2 ___
3 ___

ONE DAY AT SCHOOL ...

Marina: Hi there. What are you two laughing about?

Patricia: Leo took this photo of Bruno in class today. He looks so stupid.

Marina: Let's see ... oh, that's fantastic. He looks terrible! Send it me.

Leo: OK.

Patricia: What are you doing?

Marina: I'm sending it to the class group. There – now everyone's got it.

LATER THAT DAY ...

Clara: What's the matter?

Bruno: Hi Clara. Didn't you see the photo?

Clara: What photo?

Bruno: Leo took this picture of me in class today. Marina shared it and now everyone in the group has got it. They're all laughing at me.

Clara: Marina's not a nice person. That's horrible! You should tell the teachers.

Bruno: I don't want any problems.

BEING A GOOD PASSENGER

When we use public transport, like buses and trains, it's important to think about other passengers. Everyone wants to have a comfortable journey. It's also important to think of people who need to sit more than we do.

1 Answer the questions.

1 What different types of public transport are there in your town/city?

____

2 Do you use public transport?

____

3 If your answer is *Yes*, when and why do you use it?

____

4 If your answer is *No*, why not?

____

2 Read the comments from four passengers. Tick the comment if it's a good passenger.

☐ 1 I was here first. I'm not moving.

2 Excuse me. Would you like to sit down? ☐

☐ 3 I think that man needs some help.

4 If you don't like my music, that's your problem. ☐

3 Some people need special help on public transport. Match descriptions a–e to pictures 1–5.

a an older person ______

b a person in a wheelchair ______

c a parent with a small child ______

d a pregnant woman ______

e a person with a broken leg ______

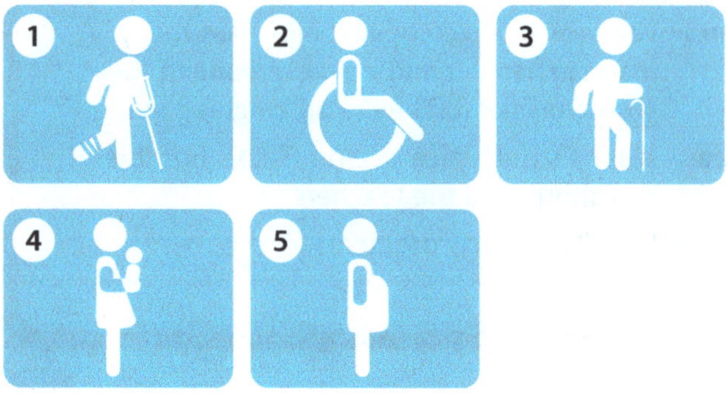

4 Look at the poster on p139 and write the captions in the correct space.

Don't sit on the floor.

Give your seat to people who need it.

Let people get off before you get on.

Put your bag or backpack on the floor.

Speak quietly.

Use headphones to listen to music.

5 Match texts A–F with pictures 1–6 on p139.

1 ___

2 ___

3 ___

4 ___

5 ___

6 ___

6 Here are some more rules for public transport. Which do you think are the three most important?

- ✗ Don't eat or drink.
- ✗ No smoking.
- ✗ Don't use public transport if you are ill.
- ✗ Don't do your hair or make-up on public transport.
- ✗ Don't try to read another person's phone.

7 Complete the sentences for you.

In general, I think people in my city **are/aren't** good passengers because ______________________________

____

______________________________.

When I'm on public transport, I try to ______________________________

____

______________________________.

On public transport, I sometimes need to remember to ______________________________

______________________________.

Make our transport system great for EVERYONE

- **A** Please think about older passengers, pregnant women, people with children and other passengers with difficulties.
- **B** Different people like different types of music. Some people don't want to listen to anything. Don't listen without headphones and keep the volume low.
- **C** We all use the underground, but we don't all want to hear your conversation. If everyone speaks in a quiet voice, we can all travel together comfortably.
- **D** Stand to one side of the doors and wait for other passengers to leave the train or bus before you get on. It's quicker and safer for everyone.
- **E** If you have it on your back, it's difficult for other people to stand or walk past you.
- **F** If there aren't any seats, please stand. If you sit on the floor, it's difficult for other passengers to stand.

Little Women, Louisa May Alcott

About the author

Louisa May Alcott was born in Pennsylvania in 1832 and lived in Massachusetts for most of her life. She had three sisters: May, Elizabeth and Anna. Louisa didn't go to school. Her father was a teacher; Louisa studied and read at home. Later, she started writing and she worked to help other women.

About the story

Little Women (1868) was Alcott's most popular book. It's the story of four sisters: Amy, Meg, Beth and Jo, during the American Civil War. The war was between the Confederate States in the south and the Union in the north. The girls' father is working in a hospital in Washington and their mother (Marmee) and the girls are at home in Massachusetts.

Before reading

1 Read the information about the author and the story. Tick two things which are similar between the book and Louisa May Alcott's life.

1 the number of sisters ☐
2 the names of the sisters ☐
3 the father's job ☐
4 the place where the family live ☐

2 Look at the family tree and complete the sentences.

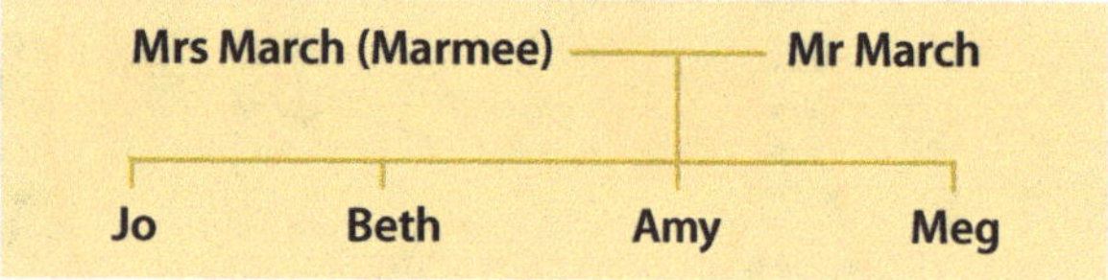

1 Marmee is Mr March's ______________.
2 Beth is Marmee's ______________.
3 Meg is Jo's ______________.
4 Marmee is the girls' ______________.
5 Mr and Mrs March have got four daughters. They haven't got any ______________.

While reading

3 Read the first three sentences of the story and the telegram. Choose the correct option.

1 Mrs March **sends/receives** a telegram.
2 Mrs March is **sad/happy** when she reads the telegram.
3 Today is **14th/17th** November.
4 The telegram **is/isn't** from her husband.
5 Mr March is **ill/well**.
6 Now, Mr March is **a doctor/a patient** in the hospital.
7 Mrs March needs to **go to Washington/ stay in Boston**.

4 Match 1–5 with a–e to make phrases about travel preparations.

1 reply to	a to the bank
2 pack	b the telegram
3 book	c a train ticket
4 buy	d her case
5 go	e a hotel

5 44 Which three things in exercise 4 do Mrs March and her family talk about? Read and listen to the text to check.

____

6 Put the events of the story in the correct order.

a Jo goes out. ___
b Mr March gets ill. ___
c Jo comes home with money for her mother. ___
d Mrs March gets bad news. ___
e The barber buys Jo's hair. ___
f Mrs March sends Jo to send a telegram. ___
g Mrs March sees she hasn't got a lot of money. ___

After reading

7 Jo helps her parents when they have a problem. How can you help your family? Think of two more ideas.

1 *I can try to cook or clean to help at home*.
2 ______________________________.
3 ______________________________.

8 Would you like to write a story about your life and your family? Why/Why not?

____
____
____

This extract tells us about an important moment in the life of the March family. One day, the four March sisters are talking about their plans for the future, when suddenly a telegram arrives.

Mrs March opened the telegram and she read it quickly. Then she sat down in a chair. Her face was white.

> **THE AMERICAN TELEGRAPH COMPANY.**
>
> Dated Washington November 14th 1863
> Rec'd Boston November 14th 1863
>
> *To Mrs M. March*
> *Your husband is very ill. He is in this hospital. Come immediately.*
> *P. Dale, The Army Hospital, Washington*

'I must go to Washington,' said Mrs March. 'I will go on the train tomorrow morning. Jo, run to the Post Office. Send a telegram to the hospital. Send this reply – "I will come immediately." Meg, Beth, Amy, come and help me pack my case.'

The three girls started to help their mother. Jo put on her hat and she went out.

Mrs March went to her desk in the living room. She opened a drawer. There was some money in the drawer. She looked at the money. There was not very much.

'I have to buy a train ticket,' she thought. 'Will the girls have enough money for food?'

Evening came. But Jo had not returned. Mrs March was worried.

'Where is Jo?' she said. 'It's very late.'

At last, Jo came home. She walked into the kitchen and she put some money on the table.

'This money is for your journey, Marmee,' she said.

Mrs March looked at the money.

'Twenty-five dollars!' she said. 'Jo, where did you get this money?'

Jo took off her hat. Everybody looked at her. Jo's hair was very short.

'Your hair! Your beautiful red hair!' said Meg. 'Oh, Jo, what have you done?'

'Many women want long red hair,' said Jo. 'I went to the barber's shop. The barber cut my hair. Then I sold him my hair. He gave me twenty-five dollars for it. I wanted to help Marmee and Father.'

Useful language

- **telegram** (n.) = a type of short message that you can send quickly *(line 1)*
- **reply** (n.) = an answer *(line 15)*
- **desk** (n.) = a table you sit at to write or work *(line 20)*
- **drawer** (n.) = part of a desk that moves in and out; you can put things in it *(line 21)*
- **enough** (det.) = the necessary quantity of something *(line 25)*
- **barber** (n.) = person who normally cuts men's hair *(line 41)*

The Adventures of Huckleberry Finn, Mark Twain

About the author

Samuel Langhorne Clemens was an American writer who wrote using the pen name Mark Twain. Langhorne was born in Missouri in 1835. Before he was a writer, he worked for a newspaper and as a pilot, helping ships on the Mississippi River. He is one of the most popular authors in the United States. Apart from *The Adventures of Huckleberry Finn* (1884), his most famous story is *The Adventures of Tom Sawyer* (1876), which includes some of the same characters.

About the story

At the time of the story, Europeans took people from their homes in Africa and took them to America. They were not free and had to work as slaves for other people. In Missouri and other states in the south, some people had slaves. Other states in the north-east were free states where people didn't have slaves. The book tells the story of how a boy, Huckleberry Finn (Huck), escapes from his cruel father and travels down the Mississippi River with a slave, Jim, who is trying to get to the free states. They meet a lot of different people and have many adventures on their travels.

Before reading

1 Read the information about the author and the story and find a word for each definition.

1 A name a writer uses. It is not their real name. ______________
2 A person who flies a plane or who helps a ship in difficult water. ______________
3 People in a story, book or film. ______________
4 People who work for and belong to other people and are not free. ______________
5 An adjective to describe a bad person who hurts other people. ______________

2 Match 1–4 with a–d to make sentences.

1 Samuel Langhorne Clemens didn't
2 He knew a lot about the Mississippi River
3 People in the north and south of the USA had
4 Huckleberry Finn and Jim have

a because of his job as a pilot.
b different reasons for trying to escape.
c use his real name when he wrote.
d different ideas about slaves.

While reading

3 45 Read and listen to the story and choose the best title for the extract.

a Travelling on the Mississippi
b Huck and Jim meet again
c Life as a slave

4 Put the events in the correct order.

a Huck smells food. ___
b Jim tells Huck why he left. ___
c Huck arrives at the island. ___
d Huck asks about Jim's plans. ___
e Huck wakes up. ___
f Jim is very afraid when he hears Huck. ___
g Jim leaves Miss Wilson's house. ___

5 Read the sentences. Are they about H (Huck), J (Jim) or B (both)?

1 He escaped from another person. ___
2 He didn't have any food. ___
3 He made a fire. ___
4 He travelled by canoe. ___
5 He felt frightened. ___
6 He felt hungry. ___
7 He has a plan. ___
8 He has questions about the plan. ___

After reading

6 Choose the correct option.

1 Jim says they have to travel at night because it's **too hot in the day/easier to hide**.
2 They travel south, not north to the free states, because **it's the direction the river is moving/people in the south are nicer**.
3 White men will try to find Jim because they **want to help him/can get money if they find him**.

7 In the text, Huck tells the story (*I* = Huck). Tell the story from Jim's perspective (*I* = Jim).

After I heard the conversation between Miss Watson and the slave trader, I felt very afraid and I decided ...

Huck's cruel father takes him to a small house in the forest, but after a few days Huck escapes. In this extract, from the early part of the book, Huck meets Jim at the start of their journey down the Mississippi.

I got to the island and I hid my canoe under some trees. I was hungry, but I didn't have any food. I slept for a few hours.

In the evening, I woke up. Suddenly, I was frightened. It was dark and there was a smell of cooking.

I saw a light through the trees. It was the light from a fire. Was my father searching for me?

I walked very carefully towards the fire. Then I wasn't frightened any more. There was somebody else on Jackson's Island. But it wasn't my father. It was Jim, Miss Watson's slave. Jim was my friend.

I called to him quietly. 'Jim, what are you doing here?' I said.

Jim looked round suddenly. He was more frightened than I was.

'Huck!' he said. 'Huck, please don't tell anybody about me. I'm a runaway.'

'Have you run away from Miss Watson, Jim?' I asked. 'Why?'

'She wants to sell me, Huck,' Jim replied.

'She wants to sell me to a slave trader from New Orleans. I heard them talking about me this morning.'

'What did you do, Jim?' I asked him.

'I waited till this evening,' said Jim. 'Then I took some food from the kitchen and I ran away. I found a canoe and I came here. Tomorrow, the white men from the town will search for me. Please don't tell them about my hiding place, Huck.'

'Don't worry, Jim,' I said.

I liked Jim. He was a good man. He was very kind. I wanted to stay with him for a few days.

'Jim, we're both runaways,' I said. 'But where do we go?'

'We go south, down the river, Huck,' said Jim. 'Miss Watson will try to find me. She'll pay a reward for me. We can't travel on the land. We must make a raft, travel down the river and live on the river. But we must travel in the dark and hide during the daylight.'

'But where do we go?' I asked him again.

Useful language

- **canoe** (n.) = a small boat for one or two people *(line 1)*
- **smell** (n.) = something you notice with your nose *(line 5)*
- **frightened** (adj.) = afraid *(line 10)*
- **run away** (v.) = leave a place secretly because you are unhappy *(line 20)*
- **slave** (n.) = a person who belongs to another person and isn't free *(line 23)*
- **slave trader** (n.) = person who buys and sells slaves *(line 23)*
- **hide** (v.) = stay in a place so other people cannot find you (a hiding place) *(line 31)*
- **reward** (n.) = money to help find something that is lost *(line 40)*
- **raft** (n.) = a simple boat without sides *(line 41)*

Northanger Abbey, Jane Austen

About the author

Jane Austen is one of Britain's most famous writers. She was born in the south of England in 1775 and had six brothers and one sister. Several of Jane Austen's books, like *Pride and Prejudice* or *Sense and Sensibility*, are now films or TV series and you can see her face on the £10 note in the UK.

About the story

Northanger Abbey is a story about friends, love and money. In the 18th century, rich English people went to the city of Bath to go to parties, to the theatre and to meet new people. They also talked about books, like the horror stories people read at that time. Catherine Morland goes to Bath with family friends and meets two new families, the Thorpes and the Tilneys.

Before reading

1 Read the information about the author and the story and complete the sentences.

1 Jane Austen was born in ______________ .
2 She had ______________ brothers and a sister.
3 In the 18th century, rich people went to ______________ on holiday.
4 At that time, people read ______________ stories.
5 Catherine's new friends are the Thorpes and the ______________ .

2 Which things do you normally find in horror stories or films? Choose the correct answer.

1 **a** daytime **b** night time
2 **a** bad weather **b** good weather
3 **a** a normal door **b** a door with a secret
4 **a** lights working **b** lights not working
5 **a** a frightening sound **b** beautiful music

While reading

3 Read the story quickly to check your answers to exercise 2.

4 46 **Read and listen to the story and match 1–5 with a–e to make sentences.**

1 When Catherine first went to her room,
2 She thought the room was
3 The first time she tried,
4 When the candle went out,
5 She decided

a the cupboard didn't open.
b Catherine started to feel frightened.
c different from typical rooms in horror stories.
d she didn't feel frightened.
e to look at the papers the next day.

5 Match the words in the box with the photos.

candle	cupboard	flame	jewels	key	wind

After reading

6 You are Catherine. Answer the questions.

1 How do you feel when you go into the room?
____
2 Do you open the cupboard?
____
3 How do you feel when the candle goes out?
____
4 Do you look at the papers the next day?
____

7 Read what happened the next morning. How do you think Catherine felt?

Catherine picked up one of the papers and looked at it. 'Shirts. Stockings. Bed-covers,' she read. She picked up another paper. 'Three white shirts and two pairs of trousers.'

No terrible secrets! No jewels! The papers were lists of things for washing!

____

Catherine meets Henry and Eleanor Tilney in Bath and they invite her to stay at their house, Northanger Abbey, a big house in the country. In this extract, from the middle of the book, Catherine is alone in her room on the evening she arrives at the house.

At ten o'clock, Catherine went to her bedroom. The night was stormy. It was raining and the wind was blowing loudly. Catherine looked round her bedroom. It was a fine room. She smiled.

'I like this house,' Catherine said to herself. 'It is different from the houses in horror stories. The girls in horror stories sleep in cold, dark rooms. But this is a fine room. I will look at everything before I go to bed.'

In one corner of the room, there was an old black cupboard. The key was in the cupboard door and Catherine turned the key. At first, the door did not open. She turned the key again. Then suddenly, the door opened. Catherine looked inside. Was the cupboard empty? No! There were some papers in the corner! Were they secret papers?

At that moment, the flame of Catherine's candle went out. The rain crashed against the windows. The wind made a terrible sound. Catherine remembered all the horror stories about old houses. She was very frightened. Was somebody outside her door? Was somebody opening her window? Catherine got into bed. She put her head under the bed-covers. She wanted to look at the writing on the papers in the cupboard. But she was too frightened. Was the writing on the papers about a terrible death – a murder? Was it about some jewels?

'I will look at the papers in the morning,' Catherine said to herself.

At last, she fell asleep.

Useful language

- **stormy** (adj.) = with a lot of rain and wind *(line 2)*
- **dark** (adj.) = without light, you can't see well *(line 8)*
- **empty** (adj.) = with nothing in it *(line 16)*
- **go out** (vb.) = stop giving light *(line 20)*
- **death** (n.) = the end of someone's life *(line 30)*
- **murder** (n.) = when one person kills another person *(line 30)*

Reading

Reading short texts and understanding the main message

EXAM SKILLS

Read five short texts, for example, emails, notices, signs or text messages.

For each question, choose the correct answer from three options.

Reading Part 1

- Before you read, *look* at the text. What kind of text is it? Where does it come from? Remember you can use pictures and layout to help you decide.
- Read the text and try to understand the main idea.
- Read the three options next to the text. Compare each option with the text and choose the best one.
- Read the other two options again. Why *aren't* they correct?

1 **Look at the text. Is it … ?**

1 a text message
2 a notice
3 an email

2 **Does the text give information about a class or a free-time activity?**

3 **Read the three options. Which is correct? Why are the other answers not correct?**

A The Computer Club is in the Science Room.
B Computer Club is on Wednesday morning.
C Students can use the school computers.

4 **Do the other questions in the same way. For each question, choose the correct answer.**

1

Hi Ruby,
Can you bring my maths book to school tomorrow? I need it to study for the exam next week.
Thanks,
Leah

A Ruby and Leah have got a maths exam tomorrow.
B Ruby has Leah's maths book.
C Leah has Ruby's maths book.

2

Quiet please! Exam in progress.
Classes normally in this room are in room 2A this morning only.

A There are exams in the room all day.
B The exam is in room 2A.
C Morning classes are not in this room today.

3

To: Luke
From: Ben

Hi Luke,
Mum can take us to football practice on Saturday. Please be at my house at 9:00 so we can get to training by 9:30.
Ben

A Ben and Luke have got football practice on Saturday.
B The journey takes 45 minutes.
C Luke's mum can take the boys to football.

4

TOURIST INFORMATION OFFICE
Monday to Friday 10:00 am–6:00 pm
Also online at www.touristinfo.com

A You can get tourist information on the internet.
B The Tourist Information Office is open seven days a week.
C The office closes at lunchtime.

Matching questions to texts about the same topic

EXAM SKILLS

Read three texts, for example, three people describing a similar situation.
Read six questions and match each question to one of the texts.

Reading Part 2

- Before you read the texts, read the questions carefully. Underline the main information in the question that you need to find in the texts.
- For each question, first read the texts quickly and underline part of a text with the right type of information.
- Read this part slowly and carefully to check if it answers the question.
- Check if the other texts do not have the answers before you decide.

1 Read the questions and underline the most important words.

1 Who does a lot of sport in their free time?
2 Whose friends all live in the same part of town?
3 Who spends free time with people from their family?
4 Who has different friends in different places?
5 Who only sees one person from school in their free time?
6 Who spends some free time in their friend's home?

2 Answer question 1 in exercise 1. Follow the steps:

1 Read the texts quickly to find where someone talks about sport.
2 Read that part of the text slowly to check.
3 Look at the other texts again to be sure this is the best answer.
4 Note the phrases that helped you decide.

3 Answer questions 2–6 in the same way.

JONAS

I spend my free time with my friends from school. We all live near each other, so it's easy to meet after school or at weekends. In summer, we go to the pool or the park. In winter, we go to Laura's house and play computer games or listen to music. And when we're not together, we send texts all the time!

ISLA

I normally meet my friends at a mall in the city centre. My cousins come, too – we're part of the same group of friends. Only one person in the group goes to my school. We normally go shopping or we go to the cinema to see a film.

ZOE

I don't live near my school, so I've got two different groups of friends: school friends and people who live near my house. I do some activities like handball and judo after school with people from my class and sometimes we meet on Saturdays to go to the football pitch. When I go out at weekends, it's normally with friends from my part of town.

Answering multiple-choice questions

EXAM SKILLS

Read a longer text, like an article from a magazine or website.
Answer six multiple-choice questions with three options: A, B and C.

Reading Part 3

- Look at the title and read the text quickly to get a general idea about the topic.
- Read question 1. Underline the most important information in the question, including the options.
- Read the text slowly and carefully to find the answer to the question.
- Check why the other two options are incorrect before you decide.

1 Complete the table with the words in the box.

day midday midnight month moon planet star sun week year

Things we can see in the sky:	Time and ways to divide time:

2 Look at the title and tick (✓) what the text is about. Then read and check. There is more than one correct answer.

1 now ☐
2 the past ☐
3 calendars in the UK ☐
4 calendars in other countries ☐

WORLD CALENDARS PAST AND PRESENT

There are many different calendars in the world today, and there were also other calendars in the past.

The Moon and the Sun are important for most calendars. Some calendars use the Sun; others use the Moon; some use both the Sun and the Moon. The Islamic calendar uses the Moon: one month has 29 days and the next has 30, giving a total of 354 days in the year.

In English, the names of two days of the week come from Sun's day and Moon's day in the Saxon language. Other days are named after Saxon gods, but the names of months come from Latin. January is named after the Roman god of beginnings and endings, Janus. The names of other months, like September and October, come from numbers in Latin.

But there are some important differences between our calendar today and calendars in the past. At one time, the English new year started on 25th March, a new day began at 12:00 midday, not midnight, and some calendars had eight or ten days in a week!

3 Read question 1. Notice the key words are underlined. Read the text to find the answer. Why are the other options incorrect?

1 What are calendars based on?
A the Sun
B the Moon
C the Sun, or the Moon, or both the sun and the moon

4 Answer the questions in the same way.

2 How many days are there in a month in the Islamic calendar?
A 29
B sometimes 29 and sometimes 30
C 30

3 Which month is named after a number in Latin?
A October
B January
C February

4 In the past, when did the English new year start?
A January
B December
C March

5 In the past, when did a new day start?
A in the middle of the day
B in the middle of the night
C in the middle of the afternoon

Answering true/false questions

EXAM SKILLS

Read a text and decide if sentences are true or false.
Five sentences are true and three are false, according to the text.

Reading Part 4

- Read the text to get an idea of the topic and what it's about.
- Read the sentences and underline the key words.
- Find the part of the text that has the answers.
- Read slowly and carefully to decide if the sentences are true or false.
- At the end, check if you have five true and three false sentences.

1 Read the text to get a general idea. Write one sentence to say what it's about.

Nishi Uggalle is 13. In her free time, she likes listening to music, but she also reads philosophy and answers maths questions. And when she was 12, Nishi Uggalle became 'Britain's cleverest child'.

Nishi and her parents live in Manchester, England. Nishi's parents came to Britain from Sri Lanka in 2001. Her mother is an accountant and her father works in IT for a bank.

Nishi could read when she was three years old. When she was ten, she did a test for very clever people and got the top score. And at school, she often studies maths problems for 18-year-olds.

Nishi wrote to the Channel 4 TV programme *Child Genius*. There were 19 children on the show and they were all very clever, but in the end Nishi was the winner. It was important because Nishi wanted to show other girls that they can study maths and physics, too.

Her parents are happy for Nishi, but sometimes they ask her to stop studying and watch TV with them. Nishi knows she's a bit different from other 13-year-olds!

2 Read the sentences and underline the key words.

1 Nishi became Britain's cleverest child one year ago. ___
2 Nishi's parents weren't born in Manchester. ___
3 Nishi's father is an IT teacher. ___
4 Nishi could read when she was very young. ___
5 Some of the other children on the TV programme weren't very clever. ___
6 Nishi wants to be an example for other girls. ___
7 Nishi's parents sometimes want her to relax more. ___
8 Nishi thinks that she's the same as other 13-year-olds. ___

3 Read sentence 1. Find the part of the text that has the information and decide if the sentence is true or false.

4 Answer the other questions. Remember, five are true and three are false.

Writing
Writing a short message

EXAM SKILLS

Write a message of 25 words or more to a friend. Include three points.

Writing Part 1

- Read the instructions carefully and underline the key words.
- Think about the person you are writing to.
- Make sure you include all three points.
- Check your writing carefully. Is your spelling and grammar correct?

1 Read the writing task and underline the key words.

You want to go shopping with your friend, Tina. Write an email to Tina. Say:

- what you want to buy
- when you want to go
- where you want to meet

Write **25 words** or more.

2 Read the email. Is it a good answer? Match questions 1–6 with answers A–F.

To: Tina **From:** Max

Hi
I want go shoping on Friday for jeans.
Max

Does the writer …

1 use the names of the two people?
2 explain the general reason for writing?
3 include all three points?
4 write 25 words or more?
5 have any grammar or spelling problems?
6 sound friendly?

A No. He doesn't say where to meet.
B No. He should start 'Dear Tina' or 'Hi Tina'.
C Yes. The correct form is 'I want TO go' and 'shopping' has got two Ps.
D No. It's very short.
E No. He sounds quite rude.
F Yes. He says he wants to go shopping.

3 Read the student's writing. Answer the questions in exercise 2.

To: Tina **From:** Freddy

Hi Tina,
How are you?
I want to go shopping on Friday. I'd like to buy some jeans. Can you come?
We can meet at the mall at 5:00.
Love,
Freddy

1 ______ 4 ______
2 ______ 5 ______
3 ______ 6 ______

4 Follow steps 1–3.

1 Underline the key words in the task.
2 Write your email.
3 Use the questions in exercise 2 to check your answer.

You want to invite your friend, Tyrone, to come to your house. Write an email to Tyrone. Say:

- when to come
- what you can do
- what he can bring

Write **25 words** or more.

Writing a short story

EXAM SKILLS

Write a story of 35 words or more.
Your story is about three pictures.

Writing Part 2

- Read the instructions carefully and underline the key words.
- Look at the pictures to understand the story. Note any important vocabulary.
- Write your story. Make sure you include all three pictures.
- Check your writing carefully. Is your spelling and grammar correct? Do you connect your ideas?

1 Read the task and look at the pictures. Which vocabulary from the box can you include in your story?

Look at these three pictures. Write the story you can see in the pictures.

Write **35 words** or more.

bus clothes decide friend get up homework same school uniform shops trousers T-shirt wear

2 Put the sentences in the correct order.

A Later she met her friend, Jo, and they both had the same clothes! ___

B On Saturday, Polly got up at 10:00. She couldn't decide what to wear. She looked at all her clothes. ___

C Finally, she decided to wear light trousers and a black and white T-shirt. ___

3 Find and underline the words in the box in the sentences in exercise 2. Then complete the sentences with the words.

at finally later on

1 ______________ Sunday, it was my grandmother's birthday.

2 I wanted to get her a present, but I didn't know what to get and I didn't have a lot of money. ______________ , I made her a cake.

3 We met at my uncle's house ______________ 1:00 and had lunch.

4 ______________ , we all went for a walk in the park.

4 Answer the questions about the story in exercise 2.

Does the writer …

1 include all three pictures? ______________

2 use good vocabulary? ______________

3 write an interesting story? ______________

4 write 35 words or more? ______________

5 have any grammar or spelling problems? ______________

5 Do the task below.

Look at these three pictures. Write the story you can see in the pictures.

Write **35 words** or more.

____

____

____

____

____

____

____

____

Listening

Understanding the general idea

EXAM SKILLS

Listen to five short monologues or conversations. Choose the correct answer from three options.

Listening Part 1

- Read the questions and options carefully.
- Underline the key words.
- Listen to choose the best option. Don't worry about understanding every word – the important thing is the general idea.
- Listen again to check your answer.

1 Read the Exam skills and the Listening Part 1 boxes and find words that mean …

1 a situation when one person is talking ___________

2 see if something is correct ___________

3 two or more alternatives you can choose from ___________

4 a situation when two or more people are talking ___________

5 most important for understanding ___________

2 Read the question and underline the key words.

Calvin's mother is calling him. Why?

A to tell Calvin to go to his German class this evening

B to ask him to do some shopping

C to ask him for some money

3 47 Read and listen to the conversation. Underline the parts which refer to each of the options, A, B and C.

Calvin: Hi Mum. Is everything OK?

Mum: Yes, but I've got my German class this evening and I remembered we haven't got any fruit. I haven't got time to get any. Can you buy some on your way home from school?

Calvin: Yes, of course. What do you want?

Mum: Can you get some apples and some bananas, please? Have you got any money?

Calvin: Yes, no problem. You can give me the money when you get home.

4 Read and listen again. Choose the correct option in exercise 2 and say why.

____

____

5 Underline the key words in questions 1–4.

1 You hear two sisters talking. Why didn't Marco go swimming?

A He had a lot of homework.

B He wasn't well yesterday.

C He can't swim.

2 You hear a teacher talking to the class about a problem. What is the problem?

A People are eating in the classroom.

B People are eating during class.

C People don't like the cafeteria.

3 Two friends are talking about an exam. What did Amy think about it?

A She thought the exam was easy.

B She thought the exam was difficult.

C She thought number 3 was easy.

4 A guide is welcoming visitors. What place are they visiting?

A a nature park

B a café

C a football stadium

6 48 Listen and answer the questions in exercise 5.

Marking places on a plan

EXAM SKILLS

Listen to a person describing a place.

Mark five places on a map or plan from a list of six options.

Listening Part 2

- Look at the plan. What type of place is it?
- Think of vocabulary you could hear.
- Listen to choose the best option and write the letter in the circle on the plan.
- Listen again to check your answer.

1 Look at the plan. What type of place is it? Read the first part of the introduction to check your ideas.

A a school

B a shopping centre

C a flat

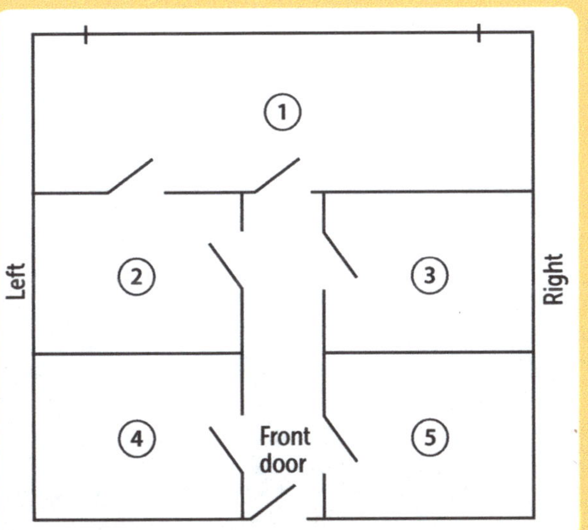

This is a plan of Nina's flat. You can see the left and the right. Nina is showing Tom her home and telling him about the rooms. They start at the front door.

2 Look at the words in the box. Underline the words you could hear in the description of Nina's flat.

bathroom	bed	classroom	door	gym
hall	kitchen	shower	station	supermarket

3 What other words could you hear? Add more words to the list.

4 Read the instructions. Write the name of a room next to the pictures. What's the difference between C and F?

The pictures show different places in a flat. Listen and write the correct letter in each circle on the plan. There is one place you do not need to use.

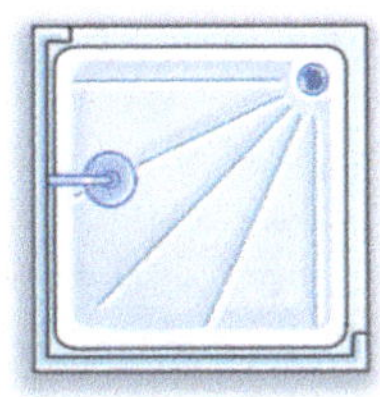

Ⓐ ______________

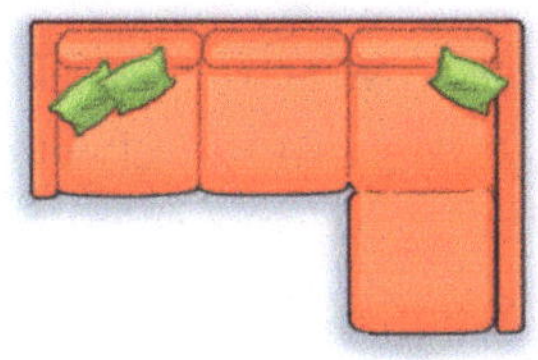

Ⓑ ______________

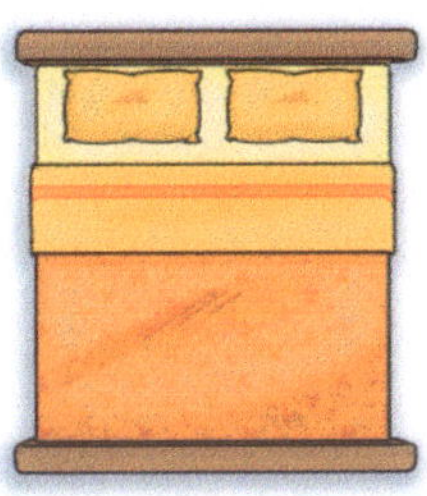

Ⓒ ______________

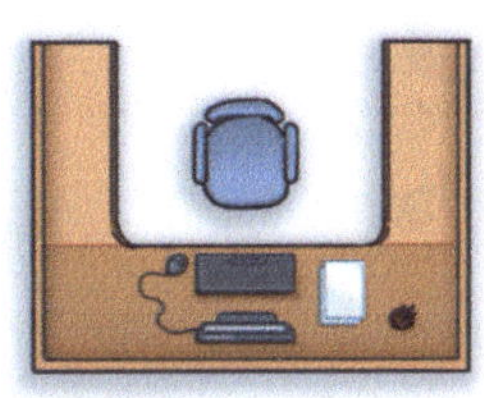

Ⓓ ______________

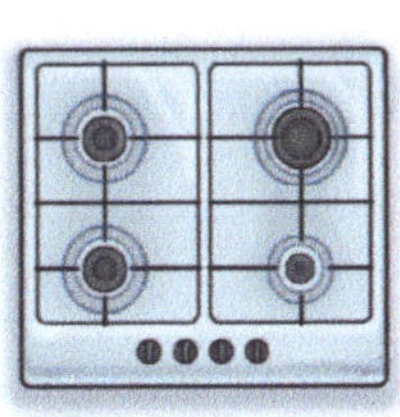

Ⓔ ______________

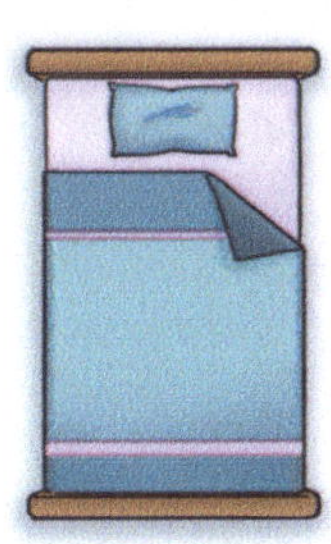

Ⓕ ______________

5 🔊 49 **Listen to the description. Write letters A–F on the plan. There is one letter you do not need to use. Then listen again to check.**

Completing missing words

EXAM SKILLS

Listen to a person giving information.
Complete gaps in a page of notes with prices, times, phone numbers, etc.
Only write one word, number, date or time in each answer.

Listening Part 3

- Read the instructions and look at the title on the notes. What is the information about?
- Look at the gaps. What type of information is missing in each one (e.g. a time, a price)?
- Listen and write an answer in each gap.
- Listen again to check your answer.

1 Read the instructions and answer the questions.

1 Who is speaking?
2 What is the information about?

For each question, write the correct answer in the gap.
Write one word or a number or a date or a time.
A teacher is telling students about a visit to a museum.

2 Look at the form. For each question 1–5, say what type of information is missing.

A a name
B a time
C a day
D a place
E a number

Museum visit

Visit to:	Science Museum
Day of visit:	1 ______________
The museum is in …	2 ______________ Street
The bus leaves at:	3 ______________ am
Who to pay:	4 ______________
The cost of the visit:	5 ______________ pounds

3 50 **Listen to the recording and answer the questions.**

4 Listen again to check your answers.

Speaking

Answering individual questions

EXAM SKILLS

Introduce yourself: answer personal information questions (your name, how old you are and where you're from).

Answer two short questions and one longer question about your life, for example, about your home, your school, your city, a typical day, etc.

Speaking Part 1

- Be prepared to answer the personal information questions: think what you can say before you start.
- Be prepared to extend your answer to the longer question.
- Practise questions you can ask if you have problems (e.g. 'Can you repeat that?').
- Smile, speak slowly and clearly.

1 Write two answers for each question.

1 What's your name? ___ ___
2 How old are you? ___ ___
3 Where do you live? ___ ___

A I'm 12.
B My name's Kelly.
C In Barceloneta.
D I'm Joe Stevens.
E I live in Miraflores.
F I'm 11 years old.

2 In the second part of the test, you hear two questions on the same subject. Read the questions. What's the subject in each pair?

1 What are your hobbies? ______________________
Do you do any sports?
2 What's your favourite subject? ______________________
Do you like English?
3 How many cousins have you got? ______________________
Have you got any brothers and sisters?

3 51 In the third part of the test, you need to give a longer answer. Listen to two answers to this question.

Now, please tell me if you like doing your hobbies alone or with other people.

1 Which answer is better?
2 Which speaker uses the word *because*?

4 Practise answering the questions in exercise 2. Say your answers out loud.

5 52 Listen to the questions. When you hear the tone, press *pause* and answer the question. Then press *play* and continue.

Speaking together

EXAM SKILLS

Talk with a partner about five pictures on the same topic, giving your opinions.
Answer individual questions on the same topic.

Speaking Part 2

- Work together and ask your partner questions to keep the conversation going.
- Try to talk about all the different pictures.
- Don't just answer *Yes* or *No*. Use words like *because* and *for example* to give a longer answer.
- Practise phrases you can say if you have problems (e.g. 'I don't understand').

1 Match questions 1–4 with answers A–D.

What can you say when …

1 you don't understand what you have to do?
2 you agree with your partner?
3 you don't agree with your partner?
4 you want to know your partner's opinion?

A Yes, me too.
B Sorry, can you repeat the instructions?
C What do you think?
D Really?!

2 Look at the five pictures. Name the forms of transport and think of any other vocabulary you know on the topic.

3 Do you like these different forms of transport? Why/Why not?

____

4 Read the questions and say your answer out loud.

Do you think …

1 travelling by bike is fun?
2 travelling by bus is quick?
3 travelling by underground is easy?

Which form of transport do you like best?

5 Answer the questions.

1 What different forms of transport are there where you live?
2 How do you get to school?
3 Is your city a good place to travel by car?
4 How do you normally travel when you go on holiday?

Unit 1: Meeting new people

- What's your name?
- My name's … / I'm …
- Good/Nice to meet you.
- You too!
- Where are you from?
- I'm from …
- How old are you?
- I'm (12/13).

US → UK

math → maths   My sister is very good at math (US) / maths (UK).

Unit 2: Talking about photos

Talking about people in a photo:

- Who are they?
- Who's this/that?
- Which is (Charlie)?
- This is (my auntie).
- That's (their sister).
- These are (my cousins).

Asking about a photo:

- Where are they?
- How old is she?

Giving an opinion about a photo:

- That's a great photo.
- That's very funny.
- That's really nice.

US → UK

mustache → moustache   My uncle has got a mustache (US) / moustache (UK).

program → programme   The TV program (US) / programme (UK) about the Putmans is popular in the USA.

Unit 3: Ordering food

- Can I have a/some … , please?
- I'd like a/some … , please.
- Would you like any … with that?
- Would you like anything to drink?
- Anything else?
- That's all, thanks.
- How much is that?
- That's … , please.

US → UK

cookie → biscuit	I love chocolate cookies (US) / biscuits (UK).
fries → chips	Fries (US) / Chips (UK) aren't very healthy.
mall → shopping centre	I meet my friends at the mall (US) / shopping centre (UK) on Saturdays.
movie theatre → cinema	My sister works at the movie theatre (US) / cinema (UK).

Unit 4: Making plans

Making suggestions:

- Why don't we (meet)?
- Are you free on (Saturday)?
- What about (Sunday/11:30)?
- Is (Sunday/10:00) OK?

Saying *Yes* or *No*:

- (Sunday)'s good.
- OK, fine.
- Yes, great.
- Sorry, I'm busy.

US → UK

practice (v.) → practise (v.)	Tim practices (US) / practises (UK) the piano every day.
noon → midday	Let's meet at noon (US) / midday (UK).
organize → organise	It's important to organize (US) / organise (UK) your time.

Unit 5: Giving instructions

Asking for instructions:

- How do you … (make an object on a 3D printer/make a website/share photos … ?)
- What's next?
- Can you show me?

Giving instructions:

- First, (go to) …
- Then, (click on) …
- Next, (open) …
- (And) finally, (click) …

US → UK

favorite → favourite	Bananas are my favorite (US) / favourite (UK) fruit.
color → colour	What color (US) / colour (UK) is your bag?

Unit 6: Asking for information

Asking for information:

- I'd like some information about …
- Where's that?
- What time is it open?
- How much does it cost?
- How can I get there?

Giving information:

- Can I help you?
- It's on at …
- It costs …
- It's open from … to …

US → UK

restroom → toilet	The restroom (US) / toilet (UK) is over there.
yard → garden	In summer, we have dinner in the yard (US) / garden (UK).
pants → trousers	I wear a T-shirt and pants (US) / trousers (UK) to school.

Unit 7: Talking about last weekend

Asking about last weekend:

- How was your weekend?
- What about in the evening/on Sunday?
- Was it fun?

Talking about last weekend:

- It was great/fun/good/awesome/OK, thanks.
- We went …
- I played …
- I met …
- I had a great time!

US → UK

go to the movies → go to the cinema — We go to the movies (US) / go to the cinema (UK) every month.

Unit 8: Buying a ticket

Asking for information:

- What's the fastest way?
- How much does it cost?
- Where do I get the train?
- What time's the next train?
- Is that single or return?

Giving instructions and information:

- Take the (10:15) train.
- Buy your ticket (at the machine).
- Change trains (at Birmingham).
- There's a train in (five) minutes.

US → UK

cab → taxi	We took a cab (US) / taxi (UK) when we arrived at the airport.
subway → underground	My dad always uses the subway (US) / underground (UK) to go to work.
round-trip ticket → return ticket	I'd like a round-trip (US) / return (UK) ticket to Barcelona, please.